The Best of MORMONISM 2009

The Best of MORMONISM 2009

Edited by
STEPHEN CARTER

Introduction by
PHYLLIS BARBER

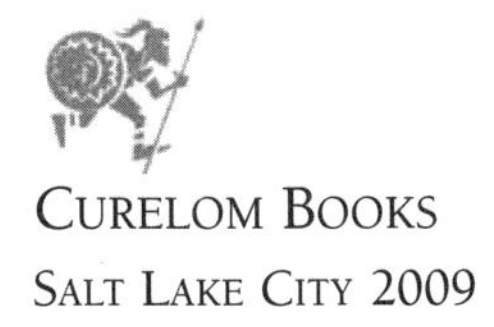

CURELOM BOOKS
SALT LAKE CITY 2009

Printed in the United States of America.

ISBN: 978-0-9843015-0-8

First published in *South Loop Review,* vol. 10. Copyright © 2008 by Joshua Foster. Reprinted by permission of the author.

"Prodigal Son," by James Goldberg. First performed by the New Play Project, Provo, Utah, 2008. Copyright © 2008 by James Goldberg. Reprinted by permission of the author.

"Who Do You Think You Are?" by Angela Hallstrom. First published in *Bound on Earth*, Parables, 2008. Copyright © 2008 by Angela Hallstrom. Reprinted by permission of the author.

"A Feeling in Your Head," by Lance Larsen. First published in *Iowa Review*, vol.47, no. 1 (Spring 2008). Copyright © 2008 by Lance Larsen. Reprinted by permission of the author

"A Sudden Pull Behind the Heart," by Patrick Madden. Published in *The Best Creative Nonfiction*, vol. 2, Norton, 2008. Copyright © 2007 by Patrick Madden. Reprinted by permission of the author.

"Nothing in Particular," by Scott Russell Morris. First published in *Prick of the Spindle*, vol. 2, no. 2. Copyright © 2008 by Scott Russell Morris. Reprinted by permission of the author.

"Solitaire," by Kathryn Lynard Soper. First published in *The Year My Son and I Were Born: A Story of Down Syndrome, Motherhood, and Self-Discovery*, GPP Life, 2009. Copyright © 2009 by GPP Life. Reprinted by permission of the author and publisher.

"How the Prayers Ran Dry," by Emily Summerhays. First published in *Sunstone*, November 2008. Copyright © 2008 by Emily Summerhays. Reprinted by permission of the author.

"We Who Owe Everything to a Name," by Lynda MacKey Wilson. First published in *BYU Studies*, vol. 47, no. 2. Copyright © 2008 by Lynda Wilson. Reprinted by permission of the author.

"Patriarchal Blessing," by Darlene Young. First published in *Dialogue: A Journal of Mormon Thought*, Winter 2007. Copyright © 2008 by Darlene Young. Reprinted by permission of the author.

CONTENTS

FOREWORD

HAGOTH.

Remember him?

No, he wasn't a Lucha Libre wrestler. Maybe somebody named Hagoth started a death metal band in Norway, but that's not the guy I'm thinking of.

I'm thinking of the Nephite explorer who sailed off into the west sea. What kind of adventures did he have? Which sea monsters did he fight? Did he shake hands with Elvis? Where did he settle—on an island, a continent, the bottom of the ocean? Sadly, we may never know. Alma 63 only gives him a few verses.

During the past few years, I've begun to notice that Mormon writers tend to be Hagoths. They enter creative writing programs, learn their trade, go on adventures, and then send their writing out into the world where it seems to disappear because, face it, few Mormons maintain subscriptions to the *Black Warrior Review*, the *Iowa Review*, the *Bellingham Review*, the *Alaska Quarterly Review*, the *Gettysburg Review*, the *Paris Review*, the *Sewanee Review*, and the hundreds of other reviews that populate America's literary landscape.

I believe that if we're going to raise up "Miltons and Shakespeares of our own," as Orson F. Whitney so famously wrote in 1888, we can begin by reading their stuff. That's why we started *The Best of Mormonism* series: to regularly collect excellent LDS writing from national publications that our community may not be aware of.

Look through the contributors' notes at the end. You'll see that we have some nationally recognized authors in there. You'll also notice that some of our writers are just embarking on their careers. Keep an eye out for them. Support them. Tell your friends about them. Don't let them pull a Hagoth and disappear. They're the ones bringing Mormonism to life in the public imagination. Let's celebrate as they lay a few more essential stones in the foundation of our literary heritage.

I appreciate the people who provided much needed help during the selection, editing, and production processes: Christopher Kimball Bigelow, Kathleen Dalton–Woodbury, Angela Hallstrom, Patrick Madden, Liza Olsen, Boyd Petersen, Levi Petersen, Carol B. Quist, Mary Ellen Robertson, Eric Samuelsen, Kathryn Lynard Soper, Michael J. Stevens, Roger Terry, and Kurt Walker.

STEPHEN CARTER

INTRODUCTION

Writing: An Act of Responsibility

PHYLLIS BARBER

FROM *Dialogue*

> You can sing sweet and get the song sung, but to get to the third dimension, you have to sing tough, hurt the tune, then something else happens, the song gets large.
> —CATHAL

YOU'RE A WRITER who loves these big, tough songs that pierce your heart and make you feel alive all over again. You believe in literature with a soul. You believe in the book that makes you think, that makes you feel as though you've been somewhere and experienced something, that you're a different person for having read it. Writing just to entertain doesn't matter to you. Writing to impress others with your cleverness or your hoped-for-brilliance doesn't matter as much as it once did. Your desire is like Chekhov's who spoke of describing a situation so truthfully that the reader can no longer avoid it. Or, in your own words, to wrangle with the tough places in yourself and your subject. Those things matter to you.

But you're a Mormon, a Latter-day Saint, and you wonder about your responsibility for sharing the gospel. You also have some deeply ingrained tendencies to be didactic, prescriptive, even moralistic at times. Having listened to sacrament meeting sermons every Sunday for a lifetime has affected your artistic sensibility and the way you think about things. You're not in the market for a lesson on the "shoulds" of responsibility nor yet another dictum placed on your shoulders. But you don't mind meditating on the idea of responsibility—what it is, what it means, whether you have a strong sense of it and don't even know it, how its nudgings affect you and your stance as a writer.

Nobel Prize-winner Nadine Gordimer's essay, "The Essential Gesture," reads in part:

> When I began to write at the age of nine or ten, I did so in what I have come to believe is the only real innocence—an act without responsibility. For one has only to watch very small children playing together to see how the urge to influence, exact submission, defend dominance, gives away the presence of natal human 'sin' whose punishment is the burden of responsibility. I was alone....My poem...was directed at no one, was read by no one.
>
> Responsibility is what awaits outside the Eden of creativity. I should never have dreamt that this most solitary and deeply marvellous of secrets—the urge to make with words—would become a vocation for which the world and that life-time ledger, conscionable self-awareness, would claim the right to call me and all my kind to account. The creative act is not pure. (p.285)

The word "sin," especially the term "natal human 'sin,'" has an ominous ring to you. Too many TV evangelists and neo-Puritan Fundamentalists, maybe? But if the word "sin" is considered in the context of suffering (in addition to its original Greek, meaning "missing the mark"), you find this approach more useful. Not only have you been the brunt of playground mentality, but maybe you've reluctantly witnessed the bully in yourself, especially when you've been snagged on the hook of self-righteousness. You've seen your sense of right and wrong in action, your sense of justice and how you've sometimes used it as a blunt instrument or wielded it without much awareness of the other side of the story. To quote Rust Hills from his article entitled "Motivation": "If we are aware of a discrepancy between our own horrid actions and our own nice selves, we can extend this realization to make a similar distinction between the behavior and the self of another."

If it is assumed that you, the writer, are born with natal human sin, that you will "miss the mark" at some point in your life, that you, too, are one of those human beings full of contradiction, then is it important that you are acknowledging, addressing or bringing greater awareness to this condition by painting your characters with brush strokes of paradox, characters whose shoes don't always match?

Is there something in you that wants to address these contradictions not only in your characters but in yourself? Does your conscience affect your sense of responsibility, and if so, how does it affect your writing?

You suspect if you want to write something that matters, you need to examine the biases in your characters which can be understood only after reflecting upon the biases in your own character. You are, after all, human. But how willing are you to look at all of what that means? You think you need to view the entire spectrum of possible behavior, not just the "good-hearted" or "vile villain" slices of the pie. You ask how your characters can be less than three-dimensional if they are to matter as commentary. Your willingness to blast into the third dimension seems essential if you want to sing those big songs or write those jagged, unpredictable stories with a real heart of gold.

In a brief look at one of Gordimer's novels, *July's People*, there are many layers of conscionable awareness. Maureen and Bamford Smales are affluent, progressive liberals from Johannesburg. Raised with house servants, they nonetheless pride themselves on their broad-mindedness regarding racial issues in South Africa. After all, she and her husband have always been considerate to the blacks, have been as gracious as they could be, and provided their servant July with "two sets of uniforms, khaki pants for rough housework, white drill for waiting at table, given Wednesdays and alternate Sundays free, allowed to have his friends visit him and his town woman to sleep with him in his room."

After a series of riots, arson, occupation of the headquarters of international corporations, bombs in public buildings, gunned shopping malls, blazing unsold homes, and a chronic state of uprising in the country, the Smales are forced to flee Johannesburg with their two children to find refuge in the bush with their long-time native house servant, July.

But gradually, as Bamford and Maureen and children become more and more dependent on the people in the bush for their survival, a series of events forces Maureen into a different state of awareness. She begins to notice much of the shallowness of her former life in Johannesburg (the shallow repartee she had carried on with Bamford and the avoid-things-while-looking-good syndrome) and how inadequate it is in these new surroundings.

She realizes that this kind of repartee belonged to a certain "deviousness" that seemed "natural to suburban life." When, in another instance, out in the bush, Maureen has to drown some kittens in a bucket and accepts it as a matter of course—a point-blank case of survival of the fittest—she realizes she and Bamford had been obsessed with the reduction of suffering but that they had given no thought about how to *accept* suffering. Bamford pities her that she should have to perform such an act, that she should have to suffer in that way. "Poor girl." He can't accept the fact that this was the best choice in the situation and that the natural cycle of life and death can be witnessed more clearly in primitive surroundings.

Finally, Maureen's shifting state of awareness gradually evolves into a state of terror when she notices the shift of power to July, whose territory they now inhabit because they have no place else to go. July not only has the keys to their car, but he drives it when he wants to without asking permission. When July decides that the gun Bamford has for sport duly belongs to someone who can use it for the greater good, Maureen's terror escalates. Power is no longer in her hands—the woman with the precious white skin that has given her an elevated place in her particular life. Her husband is ineffectual in this raw-close-to-nature setting; he can't pull the magic tricks he was used to pulling in civilization with his easy talk and trendy humor; his progressive ideas and habits seem merely laughable in the rawness of the bush country. The Smales are captives of those who were once their captives, no matter how graciously they perceived their servant, July, was kept.

Gordimer continually goes deeper and deeper into the layers of Maureen Smales' "conscionable self-awareness." The impetus for seeing her shallowness is the fact that she is losing power, that the twisting, turning knife of power is now close to her throat, and that she is at the mercy of the captor.

Gordimer spares no one. She doesn't stop with the progressive white liberals and their easy phrases, simple assumptions, and unchallenged thinking. She shows the corrupting effect of power on whoever holds that power—black or white. She probes behind the smiles and the glad handshake and the strings of euphemisms of all her characters. What lurks there? Of what are humans capable?

What did your parents tell you was important? What pearls of wisdom were tossed to you when you were young? For the woman to take no flack from men? For the woman to be obedient to the men? For the man to be the breadwinner at all costs? Did your parents tell you that the rich are a group of self-absorbed people who have no thought for those who have to labor by their sweat? Did they say that no one really understands an intellectual and that there is no audience for the truly superior mind? Did they insist that the unexamined life is not worth living or rather that life should not be examined under any circumstances?

What congenital burdens have been placed inside or upon you? What responsibilities do you have of which you are unaware? Maybe your idea of responsibility is unconscious or unknown to you. Maybe your sense of responsibility is a gut reaction to the things you've been taught and don't even realize you are living by.

What about the idea of your being an LDS writer who's supposed to be upbuilding the Kingdom of God with your work? What kind of responsibility do you have as you face the blank page? There might be a subtle narrowing of possibility before the creative process begins because of given perimeters, even though you hope you have a free and wide world to choose from which God inhabits and where everything is sacred and worthy of the literary eye resting upon it.

Can you as a writer who cares about Mormonism come to discover your own essential gesture as a writer, and might it differ from another Latter-day Saint's essential gesture? Do you reach out to the LDS society alone, or does your essential gesture include a desire to build a bridge between cultures and explore the universals? Chaim Potok, author of *The Chosen*, once said in answer to a question from the audience about how to write the Great Mormon Novel: "Find the universals, those things common to all humans."

Gordimer writes of political things which address her South African culture, but her politics resonate with the universal. Her writing is not purely political, that is to say, written to drive a point home or promote an ideology. It is meant to examine, to probe, to unearth the disparities in her culture and in its politics. Purely political writing is often purely bad writing. But if a broader definition of politics is used, such as "the total complex of relations between people in society," then political writing can be a good thing. The differentiation seems to be promotion vs. exploration. The obvious question—though the term religious writing covers a broad spectrum of quality, depth and subject matter: is religious writing a form of political writing and worth considering from that vantage point?

Italo Calvino writes in *The Uses of Literature* about two wrong ways of thinking of a possible political use for literature: (1) to claim that literature should voice a truth already possessed by politics, that is, to believe that the sum of political values is the primary thing to which literature must simply adapt itself. In other words, to claim that Maoist theory is the only valid cause about which Chinese writers can write. And (2) to see literature as an assortment of eternal human sentiments. This assigns writing the task of confirming what is already known. Basically, literature is responsible for preserving the classical and immobile idea of literature as the repository of a given truth. Consider the African writer in South Africa, for instance, who is expected to represent the tribal cause in the guise of the noble revolutionary. What about the writer who chooses to look beyond that expected stance of nobility and ask questions?

Calvino then presents two right ways of thinking of a possible political use for literature: (1) Literature is necessary above all when it gives a voice to whatever is without a voice, when it gives a name to what as yet has no name, especially to what the language of politics excludes or attempts to exclude. It is like an ear that can hear things beyond the understanding of ordinary language, an eye that can see beyond the color spectrum perceived in ordinary light. (2) Literature has the ability to impose patterns of language, of vision, of imagination, of mental effort and the creation of a model of values that is at the same time aesthetic and ethical.

After considering Calvino, you think maybe it's your responsibility to distrust politics, literature, and maybe even the way that your brain has put together LDS heritage/theology.

Further, if being a writer with an LDS background means that your writing should promote the gospel, does it also mean an unequivocal reverence for all things considered Mormon? How do you deal with difficult subjects such as homosexuality, pornography, infidelity, sexual abuse without being seen as a traitor to the G-rated and harmonious life seen by this culture as synonymous with the Kingdom of God? Does familiarity with or questioning of a suspicious subject automatically mean that a writer has fallen from the pure trajectory of white light?

You agree that you've accepted responsibilities given to you by your heritage, from your birthright, from your being in this world, and rising out of your particular society. But even if you've been born into an LDS family, is there such a thing as an average LDS family? Your parents may have been devoted to Mormonism. Your parents may have been divided over Mormonism. Your parents may have been compassionate, Christian people who lived at the edge and didn't do well emotionally. They may have lived in the lap of luxury and been exceptionally generous with their wealth. Your family may have had a good captain at the helm of the ship, and it may not have.

One example of this complexity comes from a man who always wanted to be a writer. He moved every year of his growing-up life and was always the new kid in town. His first friend was always the librarian. He was a scrappy, sensitive, shy, intelligent kid. He always stood up for the underdog fiercely and sometimes to his detriment. He never finished college, and he always talked about how he would have done so much better if he had. The LDS Church gave his family some sense of continuity, even though his father vacillated between being a religious, stable family man to one who couldn't keep a job because of his love affair with alcohol. To write about Mormonism for this man, then, would be colored by the economic circumstances, the presence of a deeply-conflicted father, the unreliable environment in which he found himself as a young boy. What would be the list of responsibilities he carried because of these circumstances? How would he, as a writer, find his essential gesture—the gift he had to give back to society?

How have you, as a writer, been colored by your circumstances? You may have grown up privileged in a homogenous neighborhood where everyone expected conformity from you and you were happy to supply it, at least on the surface. You may have grown up with no money and little hope for it and a burning desire to be seen for the splendor you wished-upon-a-star hoped you had—some kind of Queen Esther or Joan of Arc role model. You may have accepted every tenet from LDS doctrine peacefully and graciously with the hope of a rosy future. You may have challenged your parents' certainty about the "right way to live according to LDS standards." You may have seen your parents as putting you on a train on an infinite track with no windows or no doors and as a result developed a fierce attachment to the right to question any and every thing.

But here you pause. You need to interrupt yourself to ask how much of what you write is a reaction to the situation that has surrounded you. Is your writing life about action or reaction? You may be a lamb in a flock, relieved to have a shepherd, or a stubborn bull in a pen, snorting and pawing the ground, running, when you run, in circles. You've made choices of your own; you've also accepted many norms. You think your responsibility may be to move away from definition and be willing to see those things that might shock you were someone else to pass you the news. Rosa Burger in Gordimer's *The Burger's Daughter*, says that "freedom is to almost be a stranger to yourself." Maybe your responsibility is to see that the whole of who you think you are may not be the whole of who you actually are. How do you find that conscionable self awareness that sees clearly all facets of the crystal you call yourself? And then, how do you find your essential gesture, that things you have to give that no one else has to give, that view of the world, that glimpse, that angle?

Your essential gesture may include a sense of compassion for all ways of being. It may be a questioning of the establishment or an attachment to the idea of democracy that all humans are created equal and are growing to something finer than exists on this earth. You're aware, however, that this sensibility has been forged by your religion, your culture, your economic roots, your parents who had parents before them who may have been shaky citizens, proud pioneers, or denizens of the deep. And sometimes you suspect you don't have anything called a self. You have that niggling feeling at the back of your mind that "I" is a grain of sand, a letter of the alphabet, a pronoun, an entity meant to surrender to the will of God, and to follow the Essential Essence so much wiser than that of the puny self. That thought stays with you and is part of that wild bird seed mix that comes out in your writing.

All of this must be to ask yourself what responsibility you've taken on as a writer. What have you knowingly and unknowingly accepted? What is authentic to you, and for what do you care deeply? You want to use your gift of imagination. You hope it's possible to lift your experience from its limited boundaries and transform it into a unique bloom of perception.

And so you're writing what you're bidden to write, however you're bidden to do it. You are fascinated with the responsibility of being ruthlessly honest with yourself about why you are saying what you want to say and how you say it. Calvino's statement that literature and politics (and, you add, even religion), must above all know itself and distrust itself is of value to you—so you have an axe you want to grind; okay, grind the axe; but do you understand the whole of why you're grinding the axe? You want to go beyond and behind the obvious. You want that raw encounter with God and pristine creativity. You want to ask the hard questions and look in all the corners. Then, when that's all said and done, you want to let loose your imagination to play in the fields and meadows and even in the middle of the mean streets.

The Best of

MORMONISM

2009

Traveling through the Prairies, I Think of My Father's Voice

NEIL AITKEN

FROM *The Lost Country of Sight*

How we must have seemed like twins over the phone,
my father speaking with my voice, I speaking with his.
Some strange accident of genetics or the unchecked influence

of mockingbirds and mimeographs. I have heard two trains sound
almost alike till they passed, like the one last night bending westward,
the other slowing to a halt, the earth shuddering in the dark between

while the stars held their place overhead, a thousand points of tin and fire.
Had it been day, I might have seen to the far faded edge of nowhere
or whatever town lies wakeless there. Here, the wind sounds the same
blown from any direction, full of dust, pollen, the deep toll of church bells
rung for mass, weddings, deaths. Coming through on the straight road,
the land seems especially bare this year, although the fields are still green

with new stalks of wheat, rye, canola. Someone has been taking down
the grain elevators one by one, striking their weathered wooden frames
from the skyline, leaving only small metal bins. The way the disease
took him by degrees, the body jettisoning what it could: his arms and legs,

his grin, his laugh, his voice. In the end, only his eyes—their steel doors
opening and closing while the storm rattled within—and his breath,

the body's voice, repeating the only name it knew sigh after sigh,
a lullaby sung to a restless child on a heaving deck, a hush we only learn
in the quiet dark long after the boat has gone and the waves have ceased.

Believing Owl, Saying Owl

BRITTNEY CARMAN

FROM *Black Warrior Review*

> Bless the owl then, for passing
> over once more and returning to us
> the breathable air, the new, unspectacular night,
> and the world itself, trailing beneath its talons,
> and whimpers, before the noise
> and the night above the river
> swallowed it all.
>
> ROBERT WRIGLEY, "Majestic"

MY DAUGHTER'S EATING dirt again. Mouth wide, she's got the mint plant hostage behind the sofa and is shoveling handfuls of peat moss soil and pinhead flecks of Styrofoam into the dark smear of her face. She shakes her head like a bull shark feeding in some predatory, ravenous craze. I cross the floor, and she can sense me coming. Desperate, she quickens the pace. It's quick work now, and dirty. The tailings of her excavation spill across the floor. Holed up back there with dust motes, she's got two more seconds of go time, two seconds to mine this puppy dry. I round the corner of the sofa, and she's stopped short, the pendulum of her motion caught somewhere near mid-swing. She meets my eye but doesn't drop the dirt. The waters are thick with chum. Still, her movement is neither urgent nor frenzied. She slides the last fistful into her open mouth. It is a fluid, moving grace. Then, without a fight, without even a word, she leaves the plant there and toddles away. She's a smart one, this kid, and knows the drill. At seventeen months old, she's been doing this half her life.

Outside, the sky is sapphire blue. The drought shakes like a mirror from the street. It has killed the grass in our front yard and dried the roses brown. From the window, the city is wide below us. It drags itself to the mountains like an animal seeking shade. Some have called it a flower blooming in this great high desert, but like the dead bluegrass in our cracked lawn, it is scorched and withered with heat. This is Salt Lake City, Utah, where the state bird is a seagull. The glass walls of Matheson courthouse are the same blue color as the sky.

When my husband comes home he is ashen, a smoky, cinder shade of gray. The afternoon has grown dark, not with thunderheads or rainfall, just the sun sinking finally past the landlocked shore of our sea. Cars pass, flashing brake lights. They color my husband's eyes.

What he tells me is as old as the desert. Another girl has gone missing. It is the year 2004. He looks at me and says her name. My ears stop hearing sound. Holding my shoulders, he says it again. He stares gray into my face. This is a girl we know, our loved ones' daughter, and like that, the floor beneath us gives way.

IT'S HERE that I would like to say we left that night and drove through the desert to find her. I would like to say that we watched the sun rise behind us in the rear view, that we called our employers from the road. I would like to say that we joined her parents for the search in Oregon, and our own parents, our siblings and neighbors, and the strangers who came to help. I wish I'd been martyred by poison oak. I wish I were bloodied by thorns.

INSTEAD, WE SIT on the front porch and sob on the dead grass. We forget to notice the sky. We talk about going home, to pick through the woods. We say *body* like a betrayal, though we both know that it's true. We don't say the rest, the worst of what we fear has happened, because when a girl goes missing in this world, there will always be that, too. When we go inside, I check the doors, see that the windows have all been locked. I notice the dirt still spilled behind the couch and weep again. Our daughter is safe and sleeping in her bed. To the west, on the shores of the Salt Lake, seagulls rest with their heads tucked inside their wings.

THIS IS A SPLINTER, because the truth sometimes hurts. We almost left that night.

TEN DAYS LATER, we finally go. Southern Idaho lies hot before us in shades of brown and gray. It is cut by creek beds and rivers, shining water under sun. Our daughter is asleep in the back seat, her chin nearly touching her chest. I see her white head throw the sunlight and suddenly I'm squinting, hawkish, at the water because Brooke was blonde, and in the river, her hair would shine like gold.

"Do you see something in the water?" my husband asks, and I tell him that I don't.

BUT I WANTED to tell her parents that she wasn't there. I wanted to tell them that we looked, and so from the window, I take to searching the cutbanks, the tangles thick with reeds. When staring down an irrigation ditch near Ontario, a grocery bag looks just like a sweatshirt hanging in a tree. It's the closest we come to finding her; the authorities call the search off the day before we arrive.

Here is a fracture, a crack in the dish.

Here is a slate grey sliver of bone:

TWO YEARS LATER, something in the ditch bank catches my eye in the half second between seeing it and sailing past at seventy-five on this two-lane country road we call the highway here in northern Idaho. It is white and lit with afternoon sun. I crane my neck and say, trash, out loud. Some errant, swollen diaper. A dirty paper plate. But I'm wrestling out of my seat belt to get a better look, and when my friend says, what? I tell her to pull the truck around, say do it quickly. She brakes into the gravel shoulder and turns back.

The bird is lying belly up. It's his breast that I have seen, white against the chocolate dark dirt. From the roadside, I'm sure it's a hawk, Swainson's maybe, or a yearling red-tail. The kind so common here you see kettles of them riding circles over sun-warmed squares of wheat grass. A bird you might watch dress a field snake on any given day. It's a hawk, I think, not very big, fallen from the wing of his thermal, probably flung head long into the brown windshield of a muddy half-ton and dead now on the side of the road. It wouldn't be the first time. On this stretch of rural highway, road kill isn't uncommon, and more often than not it's a bird you'll find ragged, tail feathers stiff and wagging in the breeze. Here in the Idaho panhandle, green miles of wheat roll between blue, wooded rises and canyons cracked wide by river. The whole of it is trolled by crows, cowbirds, and rock doves. Flickers, kestrels, and California quail. The red-tailed hawk is a year round resident. Any trip to town and you're bound to pass some flightless thing on the roadside. In the fall, when the combines settle and the fields burn, pheasants are flattened like peregrines, lonely hearts pets.

Kim is down the embankment before me, efficient on this loose ground, and because we've both got a thing for birds, it doesn't surprise me that she's bent over and reaching to pick it up. There is nothing ceremonious in the act. It is early spring, and the sky is not yet spectacular. Cars fly past. The dirt is dark and soft with snowmelt, the white truck we're driving streaked gray from the road. I shut the cab door and wipe grime on my pant legs. My heart is knocking loose inside.

Kim has the bird like a baby, a bundle I swear she's bouncing up and down, and I've taken two steps toward her when I realize it's not a hawk she's holding in delicate, bare hands, but an owl. Its flat, heart-shaped face is white as a porcelain soap dish, an heirloom china doll. It is not bloody or gored, not hideous in any way. Its missing eye is a dry spot, a dirty thumbprint on its clean china face. But I don't take it from her. I don't touch it to feel how soft. It's a barn owl, I tell her. She nods, lays it in the covered bed of her pickup, and for a second, neither of us says anything more.

When it's time to address what we'll do with it, Kim suggests that I keep it, says a taxidermist will do it up nicely. I imagine it moldering on a bookshelf, its white breast gone dingy, its porcelain face turned gray. I tell her it would frighten my daughter who has only just turned three. Still, as we turn home, the idea is growing and buoyant, like something grown wings and ready to fly. I could keep it clean and dusted. Maybe a professional could replace its missing eye.

Ultimately we decide on the freezer. From there, we figure we've just bought ourselves some time. Better than leaving it on the roadside. More respectful, we convince ourselves. An apology. At least it won't begin to stink. We take the owl to my house, and before interring it, we decide to look at it, one last time, in the light. I still can't bring myself to touch it, so Kim is holding it up. I'm taking pictures. I have a hard time explaining why. Years ago, my cousin, just older than I, delivered a baby dead in her uterus a week. Her labor lasted three days, and when the baby was finally laid in her arms it had visibly begun to decompose. The child's skin was patchy and purple. Her lips were wrinkled black. And still, on the piano in my aunt's living room, there among all the rest, is a framed photograph of the baby, her flaking eyelids, her shriveled lips. Not sleeping but obviously dead.

The picture has always bothered me, and even as Kim is holding the bird towards the camera, I'm reminded of it. Of the way I turn my head enough not to see it, the way I hope my daughter doesn't take it down and cradle it, call it baby and carry it around as she's sometimes prone to do. Still, here I am taking pictures of a dead bird, because somehow I want to remember it, that maybe, like my cousin's daughter, it was beautiful despite the rest. But this is not a child, I tell myself. This is different. Then I tell myself again.

When the owl is in the freezer for the third week, I wake one night from a dream that my daughter has disappeared. This is no real news. I dream it every month or so; it used to be once a week. Bothered, I find my way to the kitchen. I think I will feel better if I get something to drink. The house is dark, but the moon is shining so brightly through the kitchen window that I don't need to use the light. Looking for an ice cube, I open the freezer. The owl is there silent, wedged between the ice cream and the ice, and suddenly I'm sweating. Suddenly my ears have begun to ring. Wrapped in plastic, like dark receiving blankets, it looks so much like a baby that I have to take it out. I have to look at it in the moonlight, have to see it be an owl. I pull the bundle from the freezer and try softly to unwrap. My hands work the tape from the plastic bag, but I'm still seeing a baby, and then, frantic, I'm pulling off layers, peeling them back. And then I have it. The bag is open, the owl is there.

Something rustles in the darkness behind me. I turn to see my daughter standing at the kitchen door. She asks me what I'm doing in a small voice, and for a moment, I don't know what to say. What am I doing after all? Fearing something I can't put words to? Mourning a loss I don't know how to name? She is three years old; what can I tell her when, at thirty, I don't even understand? Still there she is, sleep mussed and milk white, her hair in a furious tangle—a nest glowing silver beneath the moon. I tell her this, it is all that I know: that I found a bird. That it was beautiful. That I couldn't leave it, and so I brought it home. Is it alive? She asks, stepping to me, craning her neck to see. I pull her small shoulders in, then lift her up and tell her it is not.

OUR FRIENDS' DAUGHTER was taken and never found. We went home, thinking somehow we could help. Oregon was ripe with blackberries that summer. We found a patch of them beside a derelict sawmill. We also discovered a nesting pair of owls. They were barn owls, monkey-faced with porcelain breasts. We searched the rafters of the mill for them every day, and from then on Stella called *owl* at every passing bird, called *owl* to pass the time. In the summer heat, we gorged ourselves on berries and gave our bodies over to thorns. We slept, and owls flew in our dreams. When she is older, if she is ever to ask, I'll tell her how the summer passed uneventfully. How we looked over our shoulders in parking lots. How birds are drawn to headlights, how girls, even in sunlight, disappear.

Gather

JOHNNA BENSON CORNETT

FROM *Segullah*

I would basket the fruit for you,
from hidden houses behind leaves
and far boughs.
High on a tripod ladder, I reach,

and catalog the fruit with ants
and roots and the mountain behind,
note the girth of the trunk
and the aguapunctual movement of water.

You drift like clouds,
and boughs that bend under sturdy shoes,
and leaves that might blow away.
All this I would gather

and show you, you are one,
the mountain and tree and sky,
the child in his aerie,

the fruit, hanging from the bough,
and fallen in the furrow.

I would show you, if
I lay truth in neat rows
for you to inspect as soldiers, then,
set each part to a living place again,
would you know
who you are and when?

Reap in Mercy

DARIN COZZENS

FROM *Irreantum*

ON A MORNING in late July, six months after banker Frett Maxwell Jr. said, "It's no longer a paying proposition, Earl," a big pickup from Bingham Farms pulled into the yard. Through the open kitchen window, Earl Haws watched the driver get out, heard the truck's door latch. For a while, the driver, Winn Bingham, stood studying the old log shop, pumphouse, fuel tanks, and the hand-clutch Case tractor and several steel-wheeled implements parked against the long wall of the empty calving shed—the only machinery spared in the auction five months earlier.

The squeak of the screen door against the strange quiet of the yard's workday idleness seemed to catch Winn Bingham off guard, and his greeting came out too exuberant.

"Hey, hey, Earlie. Did I catch you enjoying retirement?"

Earl closed the distance between them so as not to have to match his neighbor's volume. "It's not all it's cracked up to be," he said, hesitating only an instant before extending his hand. Unaided by the setting and habit of priesthood meeting in the

Ralston Ward of the Garland Wyoming Stake, the gesture felt strange.

There had been no dew. In a field not so far distant, Winn Bingham's wheat combines were cutting their first swaths of the day. Already a haze of dust and chaff rose in the fresh sky.

"You went and rented to somebody else," Winn said with his peculiar smile-frown, "which I wish you'd explain to me sometime. But maybe I can talk you into helping me now."

Earl waited, curious. He knew that, in the house, Ruby also waited—curious.

"The wheat's just starting," Winn said, "and after that, beans. And with the late spring, we'll likely be in the beets until November." He looked toward the combines, then back again. "That's a lot of trucking, Earl."

From that day on, Earl never could decide how much that last line was intended as an acknowledgment of Winn's need or a presumption of his own.

"What are you stewing about it for?" Ruby said at supper. "It's a job. That's what you wanted." She set a saucer of pie and ice cream on top of the want ads he was reading, and sat down beside him. "Six-fifty an hour is a whole lot better than nothing. And right now, that's what you *need*."

"Something to buy the grub with," Frett Jr. had said as part of his advice last winter about "securing" off-farm employment.

"In the Marines," Earl said, browsing the ads, "we passed a physical, and the job was waiting for us in Korea. But now, sixty years old, I'm stuck selling Avon, assembling products in my home, doing other people's taxes."

"You're sixty-one, and you'd have to learn to do your own first."

Earl took a bite of pie, said absently, "I always figured by this time, I'd be helping one of my own kids farm the place. Some sons still come back and do that, you know. Look at Emery Bingham. Him and his old man must be tending three thousand acres."

"You could have rented to them, Earl," she said softly. "Winn offered you a lot more than you're getting."

"Winn Bingham? Farming *my* place?" He shook his head. "I just couldn't find it in me."

Sitting in the same mealtime proximity they had shared for most of four decades, Ruby placed her hand on his arm, said, "Are you sure that's the only thing you couldn't find in you?"

He set his fork down. "I'll say this for Emery Bingham. At least he didn't go off to college a dozen years more than any normal person needs and outsmart his testimony and dive off the deep end—taking wife and kids with him. And now look at him. A bishop. *My* bishop."

Ruby's hand slid atop his and squeezed. "Lyndon's a grown man, Earl. We did the best we could."

Earl looked into her bright, unblinking gray eyes and said, "Bad as it is, that's not the worst of it—wondering how I went wrong."

Still she didn't blink.

"The worst is trying to figure how Winn went right."

ON LEAVE after boot camp in the fall of 1951, in the last days of stationary threshers, Earl climbed on the bean wagon hitched to his dad's McCormick tractor and hunkered cold all the way to the rocky, sloping acreage Arvy Bingham had homesteaded on the river rim in 1914. By the time the bean wagon crossed the old tile culvert and rolled into the thirty-five-acre field at daybreak, most of the rigs pledged in the last priesthood meeting had arrived.

Two months shy of his twentieth birthday, Earl looked at the overripe beans and at the hayracks and wagons there to help harvest them, and remarked to his dad, "It's comforting to see some things never change."

"He's our neighbor," said Foley Haws. "How about we just lend the hand we can lend and keep our judgments to ourselves?"

In a show of county-fair nostalgia (as opposed to any serious intention to haul beans), stake high councilor A. Frett Maxwell and a drowsy fifteen-year-old Frett Jr. pulled up sitting high on the seat of a bright red wagon drawn by a team of parade mules.

"Sorry I'm late," said Big Frett, whose recent profits from banking and real estate would have filled his parade wagon several times over. "I had a buyer waiting all night in my driveway. War is hell," he added in his booming voice, "but that last one sure was good for business."

Later, with the dew burned off and the thresher receiving the morning's loads one by one, Earl stayed with Winn Bingham out in the field piling beans. On this particular day in the fall of 1951, Winn was especially conscious of his piling skill and kept kidding Earl. "You're rusty, boy. You maybe can handle an M-1—maybe—but you've sure forgot how to work a pitchfork."

Throughout the long morning, he came behind Earl, scrutinized every pile, offered little bits of advice. "Just go with the fork, Earl. Don't fight it." All this amid profane comments on boot-camp haircuts, on the effects of saltpeter on beard growth and libido, on his own enviable sexual exploits over the past three months. And all this around a cud of wintergreen snuff tucked deep along his jaw, unnoticeable until he spit.

By mid-afternoon, Earl had suffered all the coaching and competition and digs he cared to suffer. "So what about you?" he asked finally. Winn was twenty-four and never had served a day in the military, not even the Reserves.

Winn nudged the toe of his boot with one of the pitchfork tines. "Flat feet," he said. "The mighty military doesn't want me." Then his restless fork stopped. They were standing at the far end of the field, the distant thresher hardly audible. Still, he looked around as if for eavesdroppers before he whispered, "But if the Lord will have me, I'm going on a mission pretty soon."

During Earl Haws's long winter in Korea, that was a centerpiece of the news from home, Winn and the mission he was going on pretty soon. Every letter reported reformed habits, increased conviction. Beer, tobacco, promiscuity—all behind him now.

While Earl froze behind the steering wheel, running resupply through the Suipchon Valley, Winn prepared to serve the Lord. He bought a suit and set of scriptures with his name—*Winn P. Bingham*—embossed on the front covers, impressed sacrament meeting and fireside audiences with his testimony, attended two or three going-away parties held in his honor.

But all the build-up and preparation ended one February morning in 1953 when, at his wife's bidding, Arvy Bingham left a plate of hot scrambled eggs to take the full swill bucket out to the pigs. The eggs grew cold, then hard. That's when Winn went out and found his father slumped over the long trough.

Weeks later, across an ocean, mail call brought news of Arv's heart attack and funeral. According to the letter from Earl's mother, Etha Bingham blamed herself and told anyone who would listen that the swill could have waited. Her only comfort was having Winn home. Keeping him home, Sister Bingham claimed, was God's compensation for this great loss in their lives. And, she said, in its own way, fulfilling his obligations at home was as much a mission as any he might have gone on. So, in answer to a thousand, well-meant queries, twenty-five-year-old Winn bravely said he planned to work the farm and carry on.

WHEN EARL GOT OUT of the service in late May of 1954, the nightmare of Bunker Hill was almost two years behind him, and worries closer to home soon supplanted it.

Earlier that spring, Foley Haws had forgotten to take a water bag when he went back to burning weeds after dinner, and worked in the heat and smoke all afternoon without a drink. It was a very minor stroke, the doctor said—if there was such a thing for a man of sixty-two. The episodes of garbled speech would come less and less frequently; the headaches would ease. But he couldn't stay in the sun, couldn't ride a tractor for any length of time. And hand work was out of the question.

"Why didn't you tell me?" Earl asked twenty minutes after he climbed off the bus in Garland to meet a mother whose purse hung from her wrist like a weight and a father who had aged ten years in three.

It was late in the planting season. But Earl drove tractor until after dark every night, followed his furrow or disc markings with one murky lamp mounted on the McCormick's fender. Aside from church, he didn't go anywhere, didn't socialize, certainly didn't play guest of honor at firesides. In just seven days, he had the beans in and was all set to cut the alfalfa before it turned rank. But, as he was soon to find out, his parents weren't the only ones who had lived through a hard spring.

On the morning Earl planned to start mowing, the very moment he was riveting the last new cutter section onto the sickle bar, Winn Bingham chugged into the yard in a battered pickup, rolled to a stop, and sat a long time behind the wheel. When finally he shouldered open the badly dented door, he had one message:

"I'm in a bind, Earl. I'm in a terrible bind."

THE FREQUENCY of that refrain over the next three years made it no easier to hear—with reference to tardy plowing, planting, haying, cultivating.

"How can I ever thank you?" Winn said over and over, season after season. "I'll get my feet under me one of these days."

It was right to help a neighbor. Still, Earl would have preferred to be somewhere else when the other men turned to him on Sunday mornings, wondering what could be done for Brother Bingham. In those meetings, Winn was cast as the lone son, still grieving, and now bound to look after his widowed mother and the farm—soldiering on gamely, courageously, admirably.

The brethren in the quorum didn't know the whole story. As a farmer, Arv Bingham had been forever behind, but at least he worked at his livelihood. And he lived his religion. Not Winn. Even in summer, he seldom got out before ten o'clock, devoted his meager labors to ill-timed, soon-forgotten projects. In several years, he managed to dig one hole for a pair of clothesline posts, paint two sides of a barn, reinforce three legs of a weather-ruined picnic table.

And it wasn't grief and obligation weighing him down, but drinking and tom-catting—the same entertainments he had enjoyed in high school and most likely never abandoned even during the time he talked of going on a mission. Only now, Winn was pushing thirty, and the consequences of his choices went beyond tearful confessions in the occasional testimony meeting. Aside from Widow Bingham and the hired hand Eugenio, Earl was the only other person living with those consequences between Sundays. And his charity began to fail.

TEN DAYS OF RAIN in the middle of bean harvest, September 1957, persuaded Earl and Ruby to go ahead and get married instead of waiting until November.

"Wise move," the stake president said when he signed Earl's temple recommend. "You're what—twenty-six? Why risk improprieties at this point?"

When they got home on Sunday evening from their one-day honeymoon in Jackson Hole, his parents' house was dark. Tentatively opening the front door, they were met with the smells of fresh paint and bleach cleanser. Earl flipped on a light. Other than essentials—ice box, cookstove, table and chairs, couch, rocker—the place was empty; forty years' worth of orderly clutter and accumulation, gone. Every surface, every cupboard and corner had been scrubbed. There was food in the refrigerator, kindling and split wood in the fireplace, and, in what had been his parents' room, a made-up bed covered with a new quilt. On their first night beneath that quilt, with the glow of the fireplace reflecting off the bed's brass headboard, they drifted to sleep to the sound of rain on window panes.

Early Monday afternoon, in a weakening drizzle, a truck from the implement dealer rolled into the yard towing a brand new International 80 Bean Special pull-behind combine. Up high in the cab, beside the driver, sat Foley Haws.

"You didn't have to go and move into town in a rush," Earl said. "And we can't afford a new combine."

"You'n't the one 'fording it," said Foley Haws with his laborious, stroke-afflicted manner of speech. "I am. And if you and this nice girl are going t' farm this place, you going t' have the house. And you going t' start with a new combine."

Eager to impress his wife of three days, Earl lost no time hitching the new machine to the McCormick and greasing every joint and bushing. By dusk, the sky had cleared, and the radio weather report promised sun and warmth for the next week. With two thirds of his crop left—fifty acres of beans that had lain in windrows since early September—he was eager to get started.

At just a little past dawn on Tuesday, Earl was aroused from his third night of conjugal sleep by a vague, familiar chugging somewhere in a far-off land of rivers, canal roads, cattle pastures. Whatever it was, it needed a muffler badly, gurgled closer and closer until it threatened to come straight through the bedroom window.

Then he was awake. In a cold panic, he flung back his half of the honeymoon quilt, bolted up and stood dumbly on the wood floor, goose flesh overspreading thighs, loins, belly, chest. Blinking like a stunned hen, he fumbled for underwear and pants and shirt, fumbled in his mind to close doors, latch shutters and screens, pull blinds, throw down timbers and sandbags—anything to keep that chugging engine out of their newlywed chamber. He half-expected to hear a rapping on the bedroom window, to see a face peering through the glass. *What you doing in there, Earl?*

Just as Earl got to the kitchen, the chugging died. At the sink, he splashed water on his face, dried off with a straining cloth, and finger-combed his hair, all the while watching through the window. Behind him, he heard the bathroom door close. Presently he heard the toilet flush and the squeak of faucets. Three days married and already he knew how fast Ruby could dress.

Out in the yard, in the first sunny glow of a fine day, Winn Bingham hesitated for a moment against the dented pickup door before making his way to the front step. It was just past six-thirty, too early in the day for combining. But, with the dew, it was just right for cutting and raking dead-ripe beans, which is what Winn should have been doing.

Earl met him at the porch door. "You're out early," he said, conscious of Ruby in the kitchen, the sound of a frying pan on a burner, the door of the ice box. "Have you had your breakfast?" Just by looking, he knew Winn hadn't eaten a proper meal—or attended in any other way to the care of his person—in a week. His hair and clothes were disheveled, forehead oily, eyes bloodshot, lips dry. A rash of acne along his neck and jaw gave his whiskers the look of mange. When he stepped across the threshold, he paused and tried to tuck in the tail of his shirt.

"I'll have toast and eggs in a jiffy," Ruby said as the two men stepped from porch to kitchen. Winn Bingham turned his head robotically, stared as if confused by her presence.

"Winn, this is my wife, Ruby."

Winn kept staring, made no response when she offered her hand. "You—married?" he muttered, amazed that this passage in life should be made by Earl Haws before it was made by him.

Gradually he recovered, swallowed hard, scrubbed his face with a dry palm. "Pay him all this time," he began, with no preface, no transition, no move toward the chair Earl offered, "a full two bits better than labor wages—give him a house, garden spot, truck to drive, all the apples he wants from my trees, and he up and quits me, just like that." He reached a trembling hand, laid it on Earl's shoulder, gripped a handful of shirt. "Left me in the lurch, I'm telling you. Said he wouldn't wait no more for his money. Said he was going back to Texas."

"It's not the end of the world," Earl said, prying the hand from his shoulder, only now realizing that the traitorous ingrate in the story was Eugenio, the hired hand.

"I would've paid him," Winn said. "Soon as I got my beans out." He moaned at the very mention of beans. "Fifteen or twenty acres to thresh, and the weather ain't going to hold." This time he placed a hand on Earl's upper arm, said, "I'm in a awful bind, Earl. God knows I'm in a awful bind."

***

FOR THE NEXT three decades, Earl remembered the morning he pulled the wedding-gift combine away from Foley Haws's cedar-log shop in the fall of 1957, away from the beans waiting in his own field. He remembered the McCormick humming in fourth gear down the gravel canal road, then fifth gear on the paved county road, the combine trailing smoothly behind, remembered coming finally to the rocky field on the river rim.

When Earl eased through the gate and over the narrow tile culvert, he felt a kind of despair. Fifteen or twenty acres? Though Eugenio had cut and raked into windrows every pod and vine, there were still a full thirty-five acres to combine. And rocks were only part of the miseries of those acres. With enough water, the cobble yielded surprisingly good pintos—and astounding weeds.

Showing more loyalty than Winn gave him credit for, Eugenio had made a good start cleaning the windrows, disentangling ragweed and pigweed and corn-tall sunflowers from clinging beans, casting thick stalks into rake-swept spaces beyond the reach of combine teeth. But as was soon enough evident, he left for Texas before getting through even a tenth of the field.

Then what a breaking in for the new machine. Again and again, root clods hit the threshing cylinder like two-by-fours, kept the air around the combine clouded with powdery dirt that sifted into Earl's hair, eyebrows, lashes, and dulled the shine of brand new paint. Woody as timber, tensile as cable, weed stalks were forever wrapping around and choking shafts and drums, defiant to pocketknife blades, screwdrivers, hammer claws. Before long, overcautious of both weeds and rocks, Earl combined at a crawl, clutching every inch of every run up and down the slope. Time and again he stopped completely, set the tractor's brake against the hill's slope, chocked the big tires with rocks, and climbed over the pick-up carriage to clear weeds from the combine's parts. The tearing and unwrapping dyed yellow gloves green and strained finger joints until they ached. And though the weather had held thus far, every passing hour compounded the awareness that it wouldn't hold forever.

"Poor guy," Ruby said that night, holding Earl close. And, misconstruing the object of that compassion, Earl took comfort—until she added, drowsily, innocently, "His mother must really appreciate him."

Bad as they were, the big weeds proved a far lesser curse than the short, seemingly harmless berry weed. At first contact with vibrating machinery, the plant's pea-sized berries shook loose and amassed in the lowest point of housings and chambers. Half broke open between fixed and moving metal, fouled every interior surface of the new combine with bitter, seedy pulp. The other half made it into the hopper intact, the worst possible tare.

When berry pulp finally gummed the auger to a halt, Earl felt something he never had felt before, even in war. Under a nasty sky, the hopper was mounded with beans—beans that had to be unloaded if he was to finish this field and get back to his own crop, which waited ever more vulnerable to frost and wind. Again and again he jammed the long rod lever to engage the auger drive-belt. Again and again the forced idler effected only a shuddering, only a heaving resistance in the tractor's PTO gears. Amid chattering linkage and smoke from the slipping belt, at the considerable risk of impalement, poleaxing, or mangling, he tried a pry bar, then a shovel handle, resorted finally to kicking the pulley spokes until his heel bone felt bruised.

"Damn him!" Earl yelled into the wind. "Damn him to berry weed hell!"

Finally he took pliers and loosened the wing nut latch on the little door at the bottom end of the auger tube, every thread a strain from the weight of beans, let it slam open under the flow. As the beans emptied on the ground, he jumped into Winn Bingham's truck and pulled it close, slid the scoop shovel from behind the strap bracing of the tailgate. Faster and faster he shoveled, his motions almost frenzied, until his shirt was soaked and his mouth dry. Every few strokes he searched the field's border, hoping Winn would show up to find someone else shoveling his tare-thick beans, perhaps shovel some of them himself. The exertion would do him good, sweat some of the pickling out of his system. Or maybe, with any luck, kill him.

"He didn't show up at all?" Ruby asked on a subsequent night as she rubbed the ache from Earl's back and shoulders. "Poor guy."

Speaking into his pillow, Earl asked, "What's so poor about him?"

The rubbing stopped.

"That's what everybody in priesthood keeps saying: 'Poor Winn. What can we do to help poor Winn?' Do you see any of them out there fighting poor Winn's berry weed? Let them shovel four hoppers of his filthy beans, and they'd sing a different tune. I have half a mind to pull out and let the sorry beggar stew in his juices."

The bedroom became very quiet. "Earl," she said, "he's had a rough time of it. Lose your dad and not get to go on a mission... That's a hard blow. Everybody knew how bad he wanted to serve."

"Right."

"I remember when he came and talked to our class in Mutual." There was fondness in her voice. "We all thought he was so cute."

"How old were you? Twelve? Thirteen?"

"Fourteen and a half. Old enough anyway to know what I was hearing."

"You were hearing bullcrap."

"That's not fair. He was very sincere."

Earl rolled onto his back and looked up at his wife of almost a week. "Prodigal charmer swears off snuff and beer for half an hour, bears testimony with tears in his eyes, and girls melt. I don't get it."

She looked at him as if at a stranger. "Sometimes, Earl Haws, you're not a very nice person."

Not until the shoveling of the third hopper the next afternoon did Winn Bingham finally show. Driving his pickup with the dented door, he roared through the gate, bounced hard over the hump of the tile culvert, bumped across the harvested portion of the field, came on in a cloud of dust. He pulled up at an odd angle between tractor and combine, ran over some of Earl's pile to get close enough to be heard without having to do more than roll down his window.

"Something wrong with your auger?"

Despite an overcast sky and cold wind, Earl felt his face flush, his throat tighten, kept stabbing the wide, flared blade into the mound of beans, again and again, hoisting in steady arcs over the truck's sideboard. "There wasn't," he said, "until I got into your berry weed."

Leaning on the steering wheel, shaking his head in disbelief, Winn said, "Berry weed? In this field?"

"Yep, right here."

"Well, I'll be jiggered," Winn said. Then, after a pause, "And you didn't have a piece of tarp to drop those beans on?"

Earl stopped. One more word and he would have grabbed Winn Bingham by the shirt front, would have dragged him out and ground his nose in green-black berry pulp.

"No, I didn't have a tarp handy, Winn. If you want one, you can go get one. In the meantime," he said, pointing to the loaded truck, "You best run that to the mill, and I'll keep at it here."

Despite the slow nodding, an embarrassed look of confession crept over Winn's unshaven face. "I can't run anything anywhere," he said. "They took my license last week. For six months I ain't even supposed to go for groceries." Then he brightened. "But I can stay and combine, Earl—and let an old Marine trucker run the beans to town."

The tone was more irksome even than the thought of Winn Bingham on his machinery or anywhere close to work he could botch. On the other hand, every windrow of these beans run through the combine put Earl one closer to getting back to his own. So on a chilly afternoon in early October of 1957 he went to town with a load of hand-shoveled pinto beans. And when he got back an hour or so later, he could see, even before he crossed the culvert onto Arvy Bingham's rocky hillside, the brand new combine stalled askew in the middle of the field.

"I don't know what happened," Winn said over and over, poking his head here and there around the silent machine, thumping and wiggling uselessly, his chaotic hair blowing in the cold wind like electrified mop strands. "The dang thing just up and quit me."

As Earl soon discovered, the combine up and quit because of a rock wedged between the threshing cylinder and its sheet metal housing.

And then?

They "had words," as Foley Haws would have said before heat stroke impaired his speech.

Judas Priest, Winn.

In fact, the words Earl remembered were mostly his own, accompanied, grotesquely, by finger pointing, arm waving, forehead clapping.

The wedding-gift combine he had coddled through the nastiest beans in the Ralston Valley, without a breakdown, the machine he needed to finish harvesting his own crop, now stood idle. All because Winn Bingham's bloodshot eyes had missed a rock the size of a melon. And only a ridiculously high RPM could explain the extent of the damage: threshing drum dented and punctured, its shaft warped, bearings burned, chain links on either side of the ladder feeder snapped like candy canes.

How blind do you have to be?

The one new piece of machinery in Earl's farming career, and it would never be the same. And a week—at least a week—to get parts in and fix everything that needed fixing. And over all this hung the threat of frost and snow that did indeed end up spotting and marring and making seconds of his own beans before he could get back to them. But—no abandoning of the field, no breach of promise, no quitting, though the moment was ripe for it.

***

WHAT BECAME OF TWO MEN who farmed season after season on adjoining properties, weaned thirty-five calf crops on bordering pasture, and lived in houses not a mile apart? Two men who went each Sunday of those thirty-five years to the same church meetings, listened to the same talks and lessons, partook of the same sacrament, renewed the same covenants?

Oh, yes, Winn went back to church and changed his life, thanks mostly to his brokered marriage to the pregnant and jilted daughter of Brother A. Frett Maxwell, materially successful banker and owner of well-kept parade mules. The marriage happened in early 1958, just after Etha Bingham asked Earl to farm her husband's place the next season, just before Winn cancelled the deal. After the wedding in the Relief Society room and reception in the cultural hall, Winn and Patricia left for their honeymoon in a brand new Ford Galaxy.

After two weeks in sunny Florida, they came home to a new pickup, new tractor, new sofa and love seat—and eighty foreclosed-on acres across the canal that Earl had had his eye on. All courtesy of Big Frett.

That next August, baby Emery was born, just a week before Lyndon Haws. The two boys were blessed during the same fast and testimony meeting, baptized the same afternoon, ordained deacons on the same Sunday.

"We're so happy for Brother and Sister Bingham," the bishop said when he announced the family's sealing in the Salt Lake Temple.

Through all the years, through the births of other children in each family, scouts and seminary, periods of home teaching each other, constant association in meetings and classes and quorum projects and potluck dinners, Earl got along with Winn Bingham. Even as Winn was called to preside over him as quorum president, then as counselor in two bishoprics, while Earl found himself clerking or ringing the hall buzzer to dismiss Sunday School classes, he kept his mouth shut and never was pointedly unsupportive.

But he got along by resignation, not reconciliation, a feeling reinforced with every new farming season. As he repaired and reused and went without, Winn bought new. As he fought weeds, rocks, hard irrigation, Winn availed himself of the wonders of modern sprayers, rock pickers, sprinkler systems. Whereas Earl made a living, Winn prospered. Yet fond as Winn Bingham was of telling people about his humble beginnings, he never seemed to recall certain details of those early years, seemed completely to have blotted out the bean harvest of 1957.

In truth, though, when Earl thought back on that time in his life, as he often did, it wasn't so much the harvest that stuck in his memory—not the damaged combine or sacrificed bean crop. What he remembered was the winter evening three months later, when Etha Bingham came to the house all by herself and asked him to farm her husband's homestead the next year. He remembered her standing on the stoop in Arvy's old denim coat, with the hood drawn so tight it constricted her eyes and mouth to a small, cherry-red oval. He remembered her sitting next to the fireplace, clenching and unclenching the hands in her lap. The memory of that action always called to mind Lyndon, sitting in the same place, confiding one night not long after his mission that he didn't want to farm; then, same setting, years later, that he was going to teach philosophy at a university in

Illinois and had parted ways with the Church. Then always, always Earl remembered the last words Etha Bingham said to him on that cold January night in 1958, just weeks before she died of a blood clot in her lung. "All my life, I have tried to sow in righteousness," she said, staring into the fireplace, clenching and unclenching her hands, "but for the first time in sixty-odd years, the law of the harvest is no comfort."

***

IN LATE JULY 1992, with no other work to buy the grub with, Earl Haws, at age sixty-one, began trucking wheat for Winn Bingham and his successful son Emery. Faulty batteries and radiators, slipping clutches and transmissions, broken door latches, radios, gauges—all were things of the past. As if to remind them both of that fact, Winn assigned him to one of his new tandems, a huge GMC with a diesel engine and two upright, chrome exhaust pipes flanking its cab. "Now that's a lot of truck, Earlito. You can see why I don't let just any old wetback behind the wheel."

The people at church said, "I hear you're helping Brother Winn. How's that going?"

Ever seen so much wheat, Earlie? How about it, Earlie? Enough to fill the granaries of Egypt, don't you think, Earlie?

"He does pay every week," Ruby said one night, rubbing lotion on his back to soothe the itch of chaff. "And this isn't forever, Earl."

Wheat, then beans. August, then September. There came the inevitable afternoon when Earl saw the neat windrows stretching away below him on the rocky sloped acreage of the river rim. For an instant, a memory stirred so strongly that the leg resting in the cab of the big tandem truck was once again clutching the McCormick ahead of the one new combine he had owned in his life. The old fence was gone, the once overgrown ditch banks scorched clean with a propane torch. Piles of machine-picked rock and bulldozed sagebrush bordered a field twice as big as when Earl had seen it last.

The only thing unchanged about the field was the narrow tile culvert affording passage into it. Earl swung wide to approach the crossing squarely. Why, on a slow morning, couldn't big-farmer Winn Bingham send a few of his many hired men—Leonél, Temo, Hector—to bury a new culvert in a place like this? He had several sitting in his machinery yard. And, in the same yard, a backhoe attachment for any number of big tractors. And loaders with reliable hydraulics. Nothing patched or scabbed or makeshift. With a chain harness and a little shovel work, Leo and the other boys—maybe Leo and *Earlie*—could have this crossing fixed in no time. Then trucks getting in and out of the field wouldn't have to split inches with big tires and great weight.

"Ain't that one heart-stopper of a close fit?" said Winn Bingham, proudly.

"To tell the truth," Earl said, "it's got me a little spooked."

"Spooked! *You?* That ought to be a piece of cake for an old war-vet Marine like Earl Haws."

"It's got nothing to do with that, Winn." Earl could not keep the edge out of his voice. "The crossing is just plain too narrow."

Something flared in Winn Bingham's eyes, and the affability they had belabored for six weeks—and maybe thirty-five years before that—felt suddenly stretched to its limit.

"If you're uncomfortable with it, Earl, just say so. I'll get one of the others to take your truck across, if that's what we need to do."

"No," Earl said, swallowing the insult. "I'll manage."

On the second day in the field on the hillside, the weather changed. Daylight brought gathering clouds and a rising wind. At noon, Winn Bingham dispatched a second combine, and, spitting straw, the two big machines moved up and down windrows faster than a man could trot. Nothing slowed them—certainly no sunflowers or berry weed. Load after truckload rolled out of the immense field, across a ditchful of water running through the tile culvert.

By three o'clock, the job was all but finished—not even two

days to do what once had taken Earl more than two weeks. He thought of this, again, as he eased the GMC away from the combine's hopper spout for the last time and aimed toward the narrow crossing. He checked his mirrors. The truck was heaped, overfull, just the way Winn liked to see it. "Fill it up!" he had yelled on the very first day back in July, when Earl started to pull away from the combine, accustomed to the capacity of his own trucks. "That ain't no wheelbarrow you're driving anymore, Earl. Fill it *up*!"

At field's edge, he geared down to a crawl, inched the big tires through the last rough corrugations, across the scar of the border furrow, then up a fairly steep track toward the culvert. He could see only the upstream end of the tile pipe, marked by a tuft of Johnson grass flattened and yellowed under ten-ply tires. He would hug that end and, by so doing, would square with the other.

For an instant, after the cab cleared the deep ditch, when the full weight of the left tandem wheels came to bear on the culvert, and the tile, with the faintest wet popping, began to fracture, he thought the engine was failing. Then the big pipe collapsed, like a casket lid under a covering of long-settled dirt, crumbled beneath the tires, just fell away. The truck shuddered, groaned in its beams, and dropped with a tremendous splash. The wrenching of the frame jolted Earl's neck and jaw, slammed his thigh into the steering wheel, threw him—knee, elbow, and shoulder—against the door, and left him staring upward through a windshield that now framed only sky.

The engine had died. His fingers went blindly to the ignition switch, cranked and cranked until the battery faded. In an agony of urgency and helplessness and shame, he climbed out the passenger door, ran back around the truck. The two pairs of wheels were wedged tight, damming the flow as if cut to fit the contours of the ditch. Already the roiling water threatened the banks. The bed was tilted precariously, the frame beneath it contorted. Besides dumping a good many bushels, the drop had shifted the bulk of the load against a side panel now flexed to the point of splintering.

"You stuck good," said Hector, whose heaped truck stood behind Earl's, waiting to exit the field. He checked the crumbled culvert from several angles, studied the odd position of the tandem tires, the flooding ditch water, then whistled. "Whoo-ee, *pendejo*. You stuck good."

An empty returning truck stopped nose to nose with the GMC. The driver hopped out, curious and gawking, and added his opinion that Earl was stuck.

Then came one of the combine operators on foot. Outside and apart from the high cab of the machine he lived in during harvest season, he seemed disembodied. "I'm full, boys!" he called out. "What's the hang-up?"

Earl slid the scoop shovel from its place in the tailgate and, slogging in the overflow, began trying to flatten the ditch bank ahead of the first pair of wheels. The scoop's aluminum blade, its edge blunt and worn in an uneven concave, was no good for the job. Still, he jabbed and scraped.

From somewhere, two or three more hired hands had showed up, stood now with the others in the windy afternoon and watched Earl flounder on the water-slick grass of the ditch bank. They watched him jab and scrape, watched the shovel blade glance off sod, still brick-hard at its root, watched him clumsily check the momentum of each swing and draw back to try again.

Hector said, "Save your energy, man."

A low buzz arose among the others, and along with it, the sound of an engine Earl knew well. A dread settled into his motions, and he jabbed at the sod as if his life depended on haggling out a chunk of it. The chill of ditch water had long since cut through boot leather and socks, and was working its way upward. Then he heard the voice, measured the stride in his mind, and he knew, he *knew,* the instant Winn Bingham arrived and stood looking at his back.

"Well, Earl!" Winn Bingham said. "How did *this* come to pass?" He paused a long time, waited until Earl turned around. The voice was too jovial, too undistressed, even as the eyes took in every particular of the mishap.

"If you're all done sightseeing," Winn said to the other hands, "somebody get up to the flume and turn the water off." Then he squatted on the ditch bank the better to see the truck's undercarriage. He whistled lightly through his teeth, rubbed his eyes, the back of his neck, his clean-shaven jaw, said, "Ho-ly *cow*, Earl." Only now did impatience and authoritativeness strain the tone.

"The culvert caved in. The front got across okay, but—"

"It just up and collapsed?" Despite his smile of forbearance, a challenge crept into the question. "Drive across this thing ten thousand—hell, ten *million*—times, and it picks today to disintegrate?" Winn Bingham looked around at the faces of his crew as if the implausibility of such a thing should be clear even to the likes of them. He pointed to one of the men. "Leo never had any trouble with it." Pointed to another. "Or Temo."

Earl rested the short handle of the scoop shovel against the truck's running board, and folded his arms against whatever else was to be said. "I mean, cripes, Earl, the thing must have been here twenty years, people crossing *in*"—he swung his arms in exaggerated crossing motions—"and people crossing *out*, all that time."

"It's older than that," Earl said.

Winn turned to face him.

In that moment, the onlooking of the others registered only as a vague periphery.

Then Winn Bingham's eyes fell to the scoop shovel, and his laugh came out like a bark. "I don't know what good you think that's going to do," he said, kicking the shovel aside, hard. "As overloaded as you got this truck, it's going to take a crane to winch it free."

AND YOU DIDN'T SAY anything else to him?

Not a word. Not a wave. Not a greeting or handshake. Not then and not in four and a half years thereafter—through countless sacrament services, Sunday School classes, priesthood meetings, stake conferences. What a feat, such silence! And all the attendant dodging and plotting and maneuvering to move in the same mix of people, to travel the same roads, yet avoid every contact that could be avoided.

"Forgive our debtors," Foley Haws used to say with considerable wryness, "because they need it worse."

It all started at the crumbled culvert, which, despite Ruby's mote-and-beam logic, could not be called a little thing. Through the endless afternoon of Winn's supervision and swelling magnanimity, Earl bit his tongue to ribbons. Only because he was obliged to help, only because of that did he stay put, lightening the load onto a huge new tarp—produced upon demand, instantly—fetching blocks and jacks, tow chains, cribbing beams, slipping and flailing in the slick ditch bottom, kneeling in the muck to position and align boards.

Broad side down, Earlie. Under the axle.

Oh, how he hustled. How he worked. Solicitous. Submissive. Penitent.

But only until the truck was freed, the accident cleared, the crossing reinforced with ties and planks, the last loads of beans on their way to market.

We all make mistakes, Earl.

Only until he trusted his sore tongue to say he wouldn't be back the next day or ever again.

Dear, I don't think it's just your tongue that's hurting.

Forty years of resentment—unredressed, unresolved, unrepented of until it was almost too late, until just after the heart surgery that spared Winn, just before the pneumonia that didn't.

It was early August. Lyndon, on one of his long summer vacations from his philosophy professorship at the university in Illinois, had brought his family for a rare visit. Of late, he said, he had felt a strong desire for his children to know something of their grandparents' world—"their heritage, if you will." In the absence of beans to weed and hay to haul for old times' sake, the grandchildren played among the mostly vacant barns, amid their mother's sober warnings of hornets and snakes and rusty nails.

On an afternoon when the children's mother was gone with Ruby to Billings, the oldest grandson found the seatless motorscooter supporting a pile of gunny sacks in the calving shed. With Lyndon fishing down on the river and Earl taking a nap, the grandson somehow got it running. Using a rectangle of plywood to sit on, he started giving rides around the yard, then around the little pasture, then—opening a gate—around the cattle trails of the Binghams' pasture. The boy's circuit grew until it took in the plank foot bridge above the big irrigation flume. This was the flume that supplied the rocky hillside acreage a young Arv Bingham had grubbed out of sagebrush with a mattock. With each ride, the boy grew more daring until, with the four-year-old behind him, a too-fast approach and the bump at the plank's unbeveled end threw him off balance. In the spill, both fell clear of the scooter, hit the mossy concrete of the steep flume without breaking a bone, and hurled to the deep pool below as if on greased runners. While Earl's grandson could swim, his granddaughter could not.

As was his habit since unshouldering the management of Bingham Farms, and especially since his surgery, Winn was out riding his property on horseback, heard the trespassing engine, saw the whole thing. A pair of resolute heels in the mare's flanks, and he was there before the boy had time to realize this water was not chlorinated and he had no idea where his sister was.

Despite carrying seventy years and a long scar down his sternum, Winn went directly from saddle to water, within forty seconds, had the little girl fished out on the bank, coughing ditch water—and breathing. As soon as Winn verified lung function, he sent the sputtering boy after his dad. Then he wrapped the girl in his shirt, cradled her in front of him on the saddle, and, with the mare running full-out, retraced the scooter's route, which, given the lay of the pasture land, got him to Earl's house before he could have gotten to his own.

On a sofa by the fireplace, Earl traded the wet shirt around his granddaughter for a very old honeymoon quilt, and asked Winn to drive them to the doctor, just to be sure. A cut on her scalp was bleeding, and she had a bad knot. They were about to give her a blessing when Lyndon rushed in, frantic. He was still in his hip waders. After the retelling and explaining, he looked from his father to Winn and back again, removed his fishing hat, then nodded for them to go ahead. For one instant, it looked as if he was going to lay his hands with theirs on the little girl's head.

***

WORD THAT WINN BINGHAM is still down with pneumonia comes one Sunday morning in priesthood meeting. The news troubles Earl more than he can say. On the way home from church, listening to Ruby speak of the illness, he feels his eyes welling with tears. For a moment, he has all he can do to whisper, "Poor guy."

There is no question now about what he should do and when.

Half an hour later, still in his white shirt and tie, he stands at the threshold of a back room of Winn Bingham's big brick house. When the swinging door clears a certain point, like a stage curtain, Earl suddenly sees what he has only anticipated. On the far side of the room Winn Bingham lies rigidly in the big bed. He looks small. From a table set close by, a vaporizer sends a steady mist in the direction of his face. The spitting hiss of the steam blends with the rasp of breathing. This same table serves as a stand for a folded wet washcloth, hot water bottle, jar of Vicks, wads of tissue scattered around a Kleenex box, a bubble-like bronchial inhaler, bottles of pills and capsules, a glass of water with a straw in it, another of juice—neither much depleted—and a bedpan. It occurs to Earl that Winn and Pat have shared a bedroom just as long as he and Ruby have.

"So," Pat Bingham says, too cheerfully, moving toward the bed, "let's see if we can rouse Sleeping Beauty."

"Let him sleep," Earl says. "I can come back."

She doesn't hesitate. "No, let's let you see him while you're here. He needs to be awake a while anyway. Those pills keep him in the darnedest stupor all the time." She points apologetically to the bedpan. "He fell with me yesterday in the bathroom. When he wasn't getting any better, I wanted him home—in case . . . Well, just in case. I insisted. But I had no idea he'd be so weak. He can't even sit on the toilet, Earl."

Gently she shakes Winn's shoulder, and when at last his eyes flutter open, when she has wiped his mouth and nose after a coughing spasm, she says, loudly, "Winn? Winn, Earl is here to see you. Earl Haws."

For a moment, the eyes remain clouded. Then, when the announcement has arrived somewhere deep within him, Winn Bingham turns his head and smiles weakly.

"I'll let you be for a while," Pat Bingham says, tugging and smoothing the bed covers before stepping away. In the doorway, she turns. "He'll be glad you came."

Alone with Winn Bingham in the bedroom, Earl needs no force of habit to take the waxy hand in his own. For the first time he notices, in the V of the open pajama collar, the grizzled stubble of chest hair and the top end of a scar as thick and pink as an earthworm. Winn Bingham blinks, gags on a cough, swallows laboriously. Earl shudders at the imagined ache in his neighbor's chest and at what is not imagined in his own. Thanks to Winn, a grandson has nothing more tragic than a foolish accident to put behind him. Thanks to Winn, a granddaughter will grow to womanhood. How could such ever be repaid?

"Can I do anything for you?" Earl asks.

His words echo oddly off the high ceiling. A gust of wind rattles the bedroom's north window, against the sound of the vaporizer's warm sputtering. He waits, holding the familiar hand, less awkward with each moment, and gradually finds more words.

"Looks to be a hard winter. It's a good thing the beans are all in."

But when that hand suddenly clasps his with unexpected strength, Earl is moved to wordlessness. All that passes between them, when their eyes meet now, is a peace and a healing.

Clothing Esther

LISA TORCASSO DOWNING

FROM *Sunstone*

MARY HAD STOOD before her mother-in-law countless times before this. Stood before her more than beside her, the way Esther had always wanted her. *Help me with this roast, Mary; Come sing while I play; Read to me awhile, won't you, dear?* Most women who are bound together by their love for a man who is, to one, the protected and the beloved, and to the other, the protector and the lover, get their heads and hearts all snarled together so that neither reason nor tender feeling can be loosed to a useful satisfaction. Sometimes, though, life waters people instead of drying them out. Sometimes standing before someone becomes less a stance of submission and more a pose, a position that is neither weak nor strong, but one which simply allows the other to look upon the one. Curiosity, envy, affection, all kneaded together like dough, rising quietly in a warm spot on the kitchen counter.

Mary, you have to knead the dough with your knuckles.

Devotion: Mary and her husband Lance had taken in Esther and her husband George two weeks before George was diagnosed with stomach cancer, twelve weeks before he died, leaving ten weeks for Mary to learn to pose before Esther, ten weeks to establish the new habit of standing before.

ROUNDING DOWN, the years between the death of Lance's father and the death of his mother were sixteen. Mary had plodded along them like a tired horse on a familiar trail, passing detours and distractions with little more than a tail flick, pausing only to provide suck or to again foal. Mary had not been unhappy, and neither had Esther, who enjoyed the pleasure of sleeping a wall away from her eldest son.

And of course there were the grandchildren.

But the nights often bore down hard on Mary. Her secret fear was that the darkness—that bit which tore into her senses like soil—was attached not to the spinning universe, but to her own spiraling mind. Over the years, Mary had shared many things with Esther, a bathroom scale, sometimes a hairbrush, and, of course, the children. Yet, she never shared (wouldn't want to bother her with) every little worry or wonder in her brain, whether it popped in only every now and again or whether it had taken up permanent residence. Simple things had vanished, and though Mary swept under the table for them and hoped bleach would reveal them, she just couldn't put her finger on the simple things Esther always told the children we were on this planet to enjoy.

Certainly the path Mary trod is common, full of head colds, Scout meetings, and parent-teacher conferences, but with Esther always before her to cluck and nod and encourage, Mary moved along with a sense of purpose. She was building a family, a thing she did not at all know how to do, while Lance, especially in more recent years, was off building communication systems in Thailand or Sri Lanka, an important service in anyone's book. The difficult nights were Mary's "alone nights," and during them, she lay awake and still, staring up into the darkness and listening beyond the sheet rock for some symptom, any sign, of Esther's life—a cough, a moan, a snore, even the hummed notes of a pioneer hymn; something to assure her that all is well. Any sound which seeped through the wall or under the door into the crevices of her mind came as a sound from heaven, testifying that this path was the chosen one, and Esther, her unlikely companion.

Of course roads end—sometimes abruptly—and Esther's road was like this. An unexpected and wholly massive stroke put a quick halt to Esther's plans for Sunday dinner. Tonight Lance would've been on a jetliner to Corporate in Chicago, but instead he is at home, watching the kids watch him and not knowing at all what to do when Colleen spits at him, then locks herself in the bathroom. And Mary, who should've been at home helping Colleen with her four's times table and Marcus with his solar system report and refereeing her three teenage sons as they fight over the computer, instead finds herself standing before Esther. Finds herself staring down at Esther, staring down at her mother-in-law as she lies upon her back, is laid on a stainless steel table in a stark back room of the Village Gate Funeral Home.

MARY CLUTCHES the overnight bag, examines the green hospital gown in which Esther is clothed. She wills herself not to glance again at Esther's face, not to see what she noticed immediately: that this face she loves—with its small hump on the bridge of the nose and that old-age wattle beneath the chin, with its thin lips and elongated cheeks—has been made unfamiliar through the subterfuge of a mortician's make-up sponge.

Beside Mary stands a woman, and this woman has a voice, soft, smooth. Her touch lands on Mary's elbow, then comes a tug against the suitcase. Mary resists. That which she has carefully packed inside this bag is sacred to her and to Esther: the white gown, the ceremonial vestments worn in the temple, and the holy garment. The voice again, tender, and Mary comprehends, gives in, releases the case which the woman places atop the counter behind them.

"I'll show the others in as soon as they arrive." Another touch, this time on her shoulder, then footsteps across tile; the pull of the door and its attending, vacuum-like sensation as the woman withdraws; and then the hush. . . .

There is a moment in every life when we learn, we see, we slam head-on into the comprehension that what we always knew is no longer real, that experience is unduly egocentric, that color is subjective, and that silence cannot be where breathing is found. We have, all of us, we have said it, have said, Sit still, Hold still, Simmer down, Be still. Even God Himself has commanded it. And yet, when we face the face of death, when we see the ones we've seen every day truly stilled and made artificial by life's last word, only then do we begin to sense how hollow our minds are; how empty, how barren of things known. In that moment—that lonely, isolated, imperative moment—the only thought we can form, the only word we can hold on to, is that one simple word; that odd, unanswerable word. *How?* Not "How could this happen?" nor "How will we manage?" Only, "How?"

Right now, Mary stands in this moment; and that simple, syllable is gyrating in her mind, gathering nothing, not even a dusting of sense, but spreading itself thinly, evenly, line upon line, an anaesthetic-like numbness between reality and acceptance. Her hands remain at her sides, and yet she desperately reaches for something to hold on to, an edge into which she can sink her teeth, a ledge onto which she can crawl; something with which she can save herself from facing herself, from looking down and seeing the great nothing that becomes us. When a distant door bangs, from Mary there comes no reaction.

MARY HAD BEEN only sixteen when she married Lance, himself only seventeen. The ceremony occurred in her mother's backyard beneath a rented arch laced with crepe paper and pink silk roses. She married him before a sparse, outdoor congregation of relatives, voyeuristic ward members, and high school baseball players. The bride and groom, respectively a sophomore and a senior, were nothing more than a pair of everyday kids who had become too familiar with one another, a clumsy pair of kids who confused exotic with erotic, and who believed, for a few brief minutes anyway, that passion might transport them away from the mundane. Of the two, she loved the most, loved with a zeal she felt could heal his wounds and make him visible in the same way that heat in the desert makes the air above the road visible, causing it to wave back and forth, all silvery, and be noticed. An illusion, perhaps; but to Mary, at sixteen, illusion and vision were more than bedfellows. They were creators of life.

George had raged at his son and then wept. Esther had closed the bedroom door and stared.

It had been Mary's mother who begrudgingly made these arrangements and Mary's mother who had footed the bill. But it was Mary who paid and Mary who lived with the consequences. It was Mary's ears which rang with her mother's incessant whine: *worthless whore, worthless Mormons. Don't ruin your life. Don't marry him. No one has to know*. But of course everyone knew. They may not have known Mary's mother cursed when the girl stubbornly asked if she was coming out to the wedding, may not have realized the woman lay drunk on the sofa throughout, but still they knew. They saw. The fact was undeniable: Mary gave herself away.

Lance's father was not an educated man, but he had had sense and enough connections to land himself a career position in the public relations department of the Church during the early 1960's, about the time things were heating up. The pay, of course, was not substantial, especially for a man with six children, but it had been enough to allow him a mortgage on a five-bedroom rambler situated on a couple of acres outside the city limit. When Lance's wedding plans were announced, George cashed out the meager savings he had accumulated for his son's mission and bought him a wedding gift, a twenty-foot tin can with a bed, a kitchen, and an impossibly small bathroom. He parked it on the acreage behind the house.

His gift to his "new daughter" (he had swallowed when he said it) was a promise, a finger-in-Lance's-chest sort of promise, which he made to her as he looked Lance in the eye and proclaimed: "You're finishing school." Both he and Lance, both Mary and Esther, knew he didn't mean just high school. "You've got a family," her father-in-law said, straightening up while loosening his tie, and Mary's heart beat and beat and beat. "And you're going to live up to it." He handed Lance the key to the trailer, then walked away and around the few Relief Society sisters who remained, kindly picking up fallen napkins and emptying punch bowls into the garden. Mary's eyes followed him, looked beyond him, and saw in the distance, somewhere over the salt flats, tufted white clouds against the hazy sky. The year was 1977.

1977. . . Hair was still worn long. The bottoms of blue jeans still belled. The blacks would never hold the priesthood. The Berlin Wall was immoveable, and Mary stood before Esther in a long dress of white lace she'd bought at Deseret Industries using her babysitting savings.

Everyone had gone home in a flash, everyone except Lance and his parents. All Mary had left to do was step inside her mother's house, change into her street clothes, and walk into a new life, become a new wife, and soon a mother—a grown-up. Esther offered to help her, but of course Mary said no. Of course she said no. She said no, and her lip quivered. Esther took her chin and tipped it up, looked into her pale eyes, and they locked eyes. But only for a moment, the tiniest, briefest of moments, before Mary slammed hers shut. Dear God in heaven, how could she look this woman in the eye, knowing Esther knew all that Mary had done, that she had willingly spread her legs to entice her son, that she had robbed him of his status in the Church, had embarrassed his family, hurt them in a way that no temple sealing ceremony a year down the road could completely heal?

It was all her fault. Lance had been good—the first assistant to the bishop—he had been that good. She had never been anything, not even bad, and hardly ever present. In fact, more days than not, Mary bedded down wondering: Had the day really happened? Did she really exist? Or was her life someone else's dream?

So it was odd, the way Mary opened her eyes when Esther

said, "Look at me, child," odd the way Mary responded with both arms to Esther's tug on her hand, an invitation into an embrace, and odder still the way Mary's eyes watered and simply couldn't stop. It was 1977. The world stood somewhere between war and peace. And Mary, this little Mary who had never taken up more space than was absolutely necessary, had seen, in that fragile, unexpected moment, the world turn in Esther's eyes.

FOOTSTEPS SOUND ALONG the tiled corridor, the heel-toe click of pumps, one pair. Mary inhales deeply, smells witch hazel. The shoes stop. Another door closes, and Mary exhales, the sound fading.

She turns from Esther to the suitcase on the stainless counter. It sits between a plastic filing box and a fist-sized clock which is plugged into a socket over the backsplash. She hates having become, by default, the presiding matriarch of a family that the winds of responsibility have scattered like sand. She tugs on the zipper and opens the lid. How she does not want to do this.

But when such things are expected, such things are done. She removes two transparent packages, each marked with the rose-colored symbol of Beehive Clothing. It is her duty to clothe Esther—to hide her most intimate self—in the sacred garments, in their silky white camisole and knee-length bottoms, to adorn her in a white gown and in the robes of the Holy Priesthood.

And so last evening, after the children had finally fallen asleep and as Lance wept alone in their bed, Mary had steam-ironed Esther's hand-embroidered apron; she had carefully heat-creased each fold of the robe; she ran the sash along the length of the ironing board and pressed it to a beautiful sheen. To the temple packet, she had added her own never-used knee-high white stockings. Then today, on the way to Village Gate, she had purchased at a department store a pair of white satin slippers to replace the worn pair Esther had used in the temple each week.

Mary lays one garment package beside the clock, presses the

other against her chest. She turns back to her mother-in-law.

Four other women whom Mary trusts to know better than she how to dress the dead are on their way. But it is Esther who needs dressing, Esther who is dead. And so, with only twenty minutes between now and the appointed time of their arrival, it is Mary who steps forward.

Lance should not have asked this of her.

Her eyes traverse Esther, toe to crown. Where is the trembling hand? That forward tilt of her right shoulder?

When his father passed away, Lance had chosen not to participate in clothing him in the temple garb. His great regret remains that he cast that one last dignity to strangers. So with the pronouncement of his mother's death still ringing in Mary's ears, Lance had put his foot down. "We owe my mother this dignity." He had repeated himself at the breakfast table. And in the den. And in the car. He had even told the funeral planner, his fingers pressing tightly into Mary's waist, "We owe it to her."

Inside each Mormon temple is a place which is like no other—a quiet, veiled-in space where initiate blessings are granted, woman to woman; a place where two sisters in faith, two strangers, stand before one another, look one another in the eye and touch one soul against the other, fingertip to flesh, and repeat the words of a blessing and an anointing, the undefiled intimacy of which reflects the very depths of God's eternal love for woman, and through her, for all his children. And Mary has been there.

It is not that she is thinking of this place as she stands before Esther this final time, for the years between back-then and now have dimmed the flame of this memory. Rather, she is feeling the experience in much the same way an old woman sitting in a breeze beside the last blooms of summer feels her first kiss, feels it neither in her heart nor in her mind, but all along that tendril we call the soul. In truth, Mary is scarcely aware that her left hand is rising or that her fingers are curled like the petal of a tulip. She is barely aware that the garment package has slipped from her hand onto Esther's forearm, or that her hip presses against the stainless steel table.

When Mary's fingertips alight on Esther's right cheek, she draws back her hand—the absence of warmth, the lack of response—and takes in the whole of Esther's face. Touching again, she pushes against the subtle sag, a stubborn remainder of that grotesque twist which had marred Esther's face while she lay dying in the ICU. The skin feels cool; the cosmetics, waxy and moist.

No. With every breaking sinew in Mary's body, she does not want to do this.

Using the nail of her index finger, Mary scratches at the cleft of Esther's chin until the old age spot shows through. Grandma's chocolate drop. The children will expect to see it.

She straightens, thinks, *How?* Meaning, *How can Lance expect this of me?*

The answer comes—though she neither expects it nor feels ready to receive it—as an impression in her mind, more an image than an actual memory, more like the touch of the Spirit than a process of the brain; an answer which allows Mary to see as though through a window back to a day when Esther had stood in the front of a chapel wearing a deep coral suit with a daisy pinned to her lapel and had leaned over a coffin to bestow a final kiss. Not on George, for his coffin had been large, black, and stately.

Suddenly, as Mary envisions a long-ago Esther leaning over a small, white casket, the memory of a once-told story flows back, the tale of Lance's youngest sister, of how Lance had left her unattended in the pool at the house of one of his junior varsity teammates, and of how the angel at the top of the family's Christmas tree had come to be named Kristie: The story of how Lance had disappeared inside himself, where Mary had found him.

Suddenly it is clear: Lance expects because Esther did.

Mary dusts the white gray curls from Esther's forehead.

Sadly, what Mary most wants to know is unknowable. What is knowable, she thinks, as her finger gently twists one of Esther's locks, is that she is the "we" and has always been. Lance never knew it: He never really saw.

She places a hand on either side of Esther and gazes at the chocolate drop.

Lance had come to think of Mary as his partner, the same way he considered the two women in his domestic life a team. But Mary understands the truth: Lance may bring home his paycheck, may sometimes even take her to a movie; but the only thing which leaves him feeling truly alive is sharing the blessing of modernization with strangers in foreign places. He knows his mother baked cookies for the kids and read them Beatrix Potter only because Mary told him, but she didn't mention—and he never noticed—that Esther's bedroom door always closed at eight and that the crumbs which were left were Mary's to wipe away.

Bending her elbows, she slowly lowers herself.

Not that Mary minded cleaning up. Hers was a heart grown in the soil of gratitude, in that relief which comes from having been put alone in the dark, in the dirt, and then feeling the rain of heaven fall.

There is water here, tears in Mary's eyes as she hovers over Esther's face, looking down on the features of the woman who had showered love upon her life even though she never deserved it. A tear lands on Esther's cheek. Good-bye is so hard, so Mary waits...holds out for the miracle, for that puff of spent air which surely will arise from Esther's mouth. The fallen tear slowly tracks down Esther's cheek, leaving a trail upon her made-up face. Esther deserves a miracle.

But nature, as it most often will, triumphs over miracle, and soon Mary must exhale, must let go, must feel and hear her own breath slowly escaping her lungs, unanswered. As her exhale sweeps across Esther's mouth and nose, Mary tenderly presses her lips against Esther's cold, unresponsive mouth. She pulls back, hovers inches over Esther's face, and her soul gathers up final intimacies like the sun draws moisture over a desert pond. Then she says it, whispers it really, whispers it like a call, implores, says, "Esther?"

And the response, of course the response remains only, the

response remains nothing more than the quiet murmur of her own heart, of her own breath, of her own soul.

This—Mary straightens, wiping her eyes—*is the woman who taught me how.* With one hand, she clutches the steel rim of the table. *How to change a diaper. How to bake whole wheat bread.* The other hand comes to rest on the plastic package from Beehive Clothing which has come to rest in the crook of Esther's elbow. *How to survive.* She closes her fingers around the garment package, lifts her chin—*How to forgive*—and she scans the air over Esther's body. Though she strains to detect even the faintest aura or apparition or manifestation or sign, Mary understands that Esther is not here, that she can no longer exist in this mortal sphere except in Mary's mind, that she has gone home to those who've gone before.

Resigning herself, Mary lifts the package and tears through the plastic. Certainly the robes of the Holy Priesthood are one thing, a public thing in comparison to this. Mary holds the sacred garment against her bodice. This, Mary thinks, smoothing the silky fabric of the pant leg, is quite another. This will be Mary's gift.

THE TREAD OF Esther's foot had experienced the excess of seventy-five years of wear. The callouses, cracked and white, are all still here, on top of the little toe, on the underside of the big one, and on the pad at the base of it. Oddly, pink veins, where there should be blue, traverse the summit of Esther's foot. Her toenails are clipped, filed, and painted pale pink. Mary pinches off the memory of Colleen's slumber party, of seven little girls with cotton between their toes and seven little bottles of glitter nail polish lined up atop an unabridged dictionary. Those cotton balls had been Esther's idea. She begins with Esther's right foot. Mary gathers up her courage as she gathers up one leg of the garment bottom, and then loops the fabric over Esther's toes, which point straight up, a position which seems unnatural considering her state of repose. Enough space exists between Esther's feet so that Mary's right hand slips between them nicely.

Next Mary wills the fingers of her left hand to temporarily release the fabric. She then slides the palm of her hand into the narrow space between the steel table and Esther's ankle. She lifts: The tendon gives, startling Mary, who had supposed *rigor mortis* to be a permanent state for the human dead. But after a closed-eye moment in which she regroups her determination and chastises herself for the uneasiness in her stomach, she continues, lifting the foot with one hand and sliding the garment past the heel with the other. The foot is not light, but the act is easier to perform than she anticipated. She takes heart, then repeats the motion on Esther's left side.

With Esther's feet properly through the legs of the sacred garment, Mary surveys the situation. Esther's legs are shaved and the skin loose, especially about her knees, but Mary realizes that the thighs beneath the hospital gown remain a formidable obstacle. She hooks both thumbs and each finger into opposite sides of Esther's right garment leg and pulls it to where the calf meets steel. Perhaps this gift Mary is offering is only a weak outward sign of what she feels for Esther—Mary does the same with the left leg—but at least it is discernible. With her task on the left side likewise completed, Mary hunches down and force-wiggles the garment between Esther's calf and the steel. Clothing Esther would be easier with someone there to lift the leg, but Mary will not have her gift diminished. In this world in which so little can be known, discernible becomes certainty enough. Therefore Mary continues alone, successfully tugging the hem of each garment leg to the appropriate spot three inches over each kneecap.

From here on, Mary's hands move in secret beneath the hospital gown, pulling, tugging, urging this to end. Thread at a seam pops quietly as Mary contends resolutely with Esther's bulk. In this effort to raise honor to Esther's most private and sacred self, Mary is discovering that the weight of death is a much heavier burden than she ever could have known.

THE TIME WILL collapse before Mary knows it, and the four women whom she invited to assist her in clothing Esther will arrive, respectfully clad, reverently hushed, shown in by the rail-thin woman who had touched Mary's shoulder. These five will find Mary sitting on the cold, tile floor, her legs extended, her head propped against one of the steel table legs. Her eyes will be wide, red; her cheeks damp, and her hair out of place. The four women, her friends, will rush to her, cooing words of comfort, words like, "Mary, oh Mary, you know this is too hard," "Mary, you shouldn't have come alone," and "Sweet Mary, how Esther must have loved you."

The mortuary hostess will roll over a chair for Mary, and the sisters from the Church will insist she elevate herself and sit. So she will. The reward for her obedience will be the feel of their soft hands on her shoulders and hair. She will nod that she is all right. Of course she is; yes, all is well. The hostess will leave them. All is well.

"We should pray," one of the sisters will suggest, and Mary will watch them bow their heads.

But she will not join them. Instead Mary will sit in the black chair on caster wheels and stare at this closing rendition of Esther, at her legs left splayed and her hair mussed, at the hospital gown smoothed as flat as Mary could manage. The prayer will end swiftly, and the women will turn their attention to the overnight bag and to the white gown and the robes of the Holy Priesthood which remain inside it, undisturbed. Mary, who will use her feet to glide the chair out of their way, will make herself look on their faces as they raise the hem of Esther's hospital gown and gasp, as they pull the green, cotton fabric from her shoulder and whisper in worried glances, as they see for themselves how Mary's good intentions measure against death.

"Oh, Mary," one of them will murmur, "you can't do this alone."

Mary, whose chair will then rest near Esther's feet, will flick her gaze from the face of this known stranger down to Esther's strange face and remember the last time she had sat beside her. An IV had been dripping while monitors recorded what had seemed important. Though the medical staff had worked, though the priesthood had blessed, though Mary and Lance had prayed, Esther's eyes had still rolled heavenward and fixed themselves eternally there. Only then had Lance put his arm around Mary and led her, weeping, from the ICU.

Today Mary will find no comfort except that which comes from wrapping her own arms about herself. She will cringe as her friends jointly push, pull, and shove the woman she loves into positions amenable to dressing a corpse. The ladies will be discreet, of course, will avert their eyes, will not see what only Mary sees, given her vantage point in the chair, when, during that first violent roll, Esther's hospital gown defies decorum in favor of gravity, opening a glimpse of Esther's faded pubic region. Instantly Mary will think of Lance, of where he came from, bloodied and wet; instantly she will feel in her groin a dark shadow, the black press, which marks the descent of a child; and then, almost as though the one hunted the other, an image of the battered Christ standing before those cursed souls who cast lots for his vesture. Each image, each worry, each fear will tear into her as that cruel and familiar bit has, for decades, torn into her confidence; will tear in and grind out the words, *"You can't do this alone,"* will scrape her insides, *"You can't do this alone,"* will remind her, *"You can't do this..."*

But sometimes the voice that resounds in the heart is louder than the one that sounds in the mind. Sometimes words are whispered from soul to soul, from sphere to sphere, and can be heard only when we hold still, sit still, keep the wheels beneath us from turning, and listen for what lives beyond the veil. Such whisperings, such transparent and flawless communication, will come to Mary today, will set a diamond wall around the part within her that is brilliant and divine; will be here soon, will promise her, will say, *"My beloved child, there is no other way."*

And suddenly she will have enough of looking. She will not finish watching the women as they amend what she was unable to do correctly herself, as they tug the seat of Esther's garment bottom over her nakedness. Nor will she endure witnessing them untangle the stranglehold that the garment camisole has upon Esther's neck. Instead, Mary will close her eyes, seal them against the nightmare before her, preferring to imagine herself many miles away and many years ago, standing in a temple at the base of a mountain, a temple made golden by the lights which shine at night, wearing a slitted gown and feeling the press of fingers at her hip as a blessing and an anointing is bestowed. She will return in her mind to the small trailer, to the fold-away bed, and to the memory of that first set of tiny pink fingers kneading her breast while a matching tiny, pink mouth drinks in life. She will look up in both places, in both times, and beside her she will see her husband. Of course she will see Lance. But before him, before her, she will always see Esther.

God Damned the Land But Lifted the People; Or, A Redemption in Three Levitations

JOSHUA FOSTER

FROM *South Loop Review*

I

THE HILLS on which sit my father's farms don't roll; rather, they pillow and hunker down among the mountains' shadows not willing to rise and become mountains themselves but opting to squat along the base of the ranges and grow varieties of potatoes and wheat and beer barley and dairy hay. The hills ascend and escape eastward up the highway towards legions of tourists in Swan Valley and Jackson Hole. The hills never want attention—never strive for anything but to house the crops that feed the world, or at least the rest of the county. If there's ever a road sign that says "Scenic Idaho" it's because we put it there. Those don't grow naturally.

The land wasn't always this way, so motivated, so cultivated. Only four generations ago, the Mormons arrived at the tucked away cottonwoods along the banks of the Snake River, big mountain sage and prairie grass then covering the hills. God's Chosen began to clear away the land and dig ditches and diversions, systematically checker-boarding the floodplain with canals ten feet wide, five feet deep. They installed head gates to regulate water flow, dams to direct it to the fields. They herded liquid survival across the high desert to their neighbors and brothers. Before the Mormons arrived, the ground was barren and cursed, but they made it paradisiacal.

But all was not perfect. No matter how righteous, the Mormons couldn't coax water to flow up the Snake's canyon walls and convert the hills. Instead they labored in the lowlands, fighting ancient riverbeds that had filled their land with stone and silt. They knew the lowlands provided survival, but to make the hills grow would promise exaltation. The hills remained dusty and dry for years.

MY FATHER TELLS ME that the world changed in 1950 when a brave well digger, straddling a bucket, was lowered down a recently dug shaft one hundred and fifty feet deep in the hills above Ririe. When they pulled him out, he claimed the shaft opened up into a gigantic cavern and that a river raged underneath them. My father was born in 1957; by then, his father was piping water up the hills from the huge aquifer.

My grandfather started out with three hundred and twenty acres of dryfarm land that refused to produce unless enough rain fell, which was rare. The whole operation was sketchy; their machinery repair shop was a retired school bus, his only hired help, a Navajo named Woody. Things were tough going until George Lovell struck water. After that, everyone knew the dryfarm fields, burnt thin and golden year after year, would finally produce.

The discovery brought more well diggers and pump salesmen and power poles. The ground became a fecund soil. Men came with large field equipment. Irrigation stores began to pepper the valley. John Deeres and aluminum pipelines replaced the mules and rubber hoses. And change—conversion, if you will—poured in like a flood.

TUCKED AWAY in my mother's library is a tattered shoe box filled with photos of my childhood. We lived in the valley to be closer to town though my father's business had flourished and grown and his land now spread across the county. I'm sure my growing up is common still within the rurality of America; I'm not unique in that sense. The country kid is not yet extinct. We had our fun, my cousins and I, swimming in irrigation canals and jumping from bridges, barns, and tree limbs.

While fishing through the box of photos, I was startled completely by one shot. Sheathed in neon green sweatpants, a blue sweater featuring a motorcycle, a pair of pink ski gloves, and a neck-warmer the color of a highway caution cone, I'm leaping from our roof into two feet of snow below. My location intrigues me. I've jumped, my mother clicking the shutter right as I stepped off. My form is like Christ on the cross; legs pegged at the ankles, arms outstretched to a T. The difference between Jesus and me, my palms point down. My shaggy brown hair stands on end. The roof's eave is right behind my knees—she caught me mid-fall, and I'm frozen, hovering ten feet above the drift.

I don't know if it's my hands, the way they hang parallel above the backyard, or if it's the stupid open-mouthed grin that makes me think. If I were something else—some breed of wintertime grasshopper, an enormous desert jackrabbit—the picture could be me springing instead of falling. But memory solidifies the fact that gravity and my childhood were grounding me without a second's hesitation. Still that look as I peek at the ground from high above seems to say, Going up?

ON OUR DEAD-END country road, we spent endless hours shooting animals. If we weren't jumping our bikes or leaping from bridges or sliding down haystacks, we were hunting. All of us were given pellet guns at eight; twenty-twos at twelve. We took no prisoners. My father had one rule: no red-breasted robins—they ate the hay aphids and for that should be spared. I never told him that one day I got seven in ten shots.

We had the whole place staked out: Magpie Heaven, a stand of cottonwoods in the Finn's hayfield; an elusive muskrat lived at the kink in the Dry Bed canal; a ball of garter snakes thrived underneath a discarded fridge in the dump. We rode our bicycles to the locations every day and shot whatever moved.

One time, a Salt Lake cousin shot a tree squirrel that Marshall and I didn't even see. When he came back to the truck, he held it up by its tail and said something about a true woodsman keeps a keen eye. We nodded in agreement—even though he was from the city, his imparted adage would be useful. When the truck fired up and we bumped across the hayfield, we all felt like Daniel Boone.

JORGE LUIS BORGES ARGUES that the river is time and time the river. As such, the farms had flowed away from the flood irrigation and now almost all pumped the water and irrigated with sprinkler pipes. The investments the farmers had to make were incredible. They flattened the dikes, bought and buried foot-wide expensive steel mainline pipe to carry the water from the ditch. They purchased hundreds of aluminum connector pipes, three inches in diameter, forty feet long, with a sprinkler stand in the middle to lie out in the crop. With the improvement, the farmer didn't have to regulate canals every waking minute. He could attach the connector pipes in a line, turn on an industrial-sized pump, and sprinkle his crop in twelve hour increments. He could sleep the whole night with his wife rather than wake up at three in the morning to change a dam. Armies of Mexicans marched to the farms anticipating unlimited work—they weren't disappointed.

The first summer that I had to work, I moved two handlines,

each with thirty-two pipe, at six in the morning and six at night, seven days a week. The lines stopped twice to cut the hay. We spent the middays shooting animals and swimming. Moving pipe was a miserable job in that it was tedious and taxing. Unlatch a pipe, pick it up, walk it twenty yards, latch it, return, repeat. Flies swarmed eyes, mosquitoes feasted freely as human hands were occupied with hefting. In the morning, the pipes were ice-cold with canal water; by evening, the tin cooked from the summer sun.

Sometimes Marshall and I would move our lines together so we could talk as we worked. Once while walking home, we chased a mouse out from the hay, and it ran under the apple trees in my backyard. Instinctually, we flew after it. It scurried for a small tree along the fence. When we closed in, its random, sporadic movements—the unpredictable flightiness of it—made me nervous. I stayed back. Marshall lunged, got its tail, and lifted it up for me to see. The rodent curled and bit him on the end of his index finger. He dropped it, and it scampered away. Marshall held up the finger and squeezed pinpricks of blood from the tip. They weren't supposed to fight back, I was thinking. They never had before.

HISTORICALLY, rodents have always been a bane to earth's inhabitants. Their first appearance in text, according to Charles Elton, author of *Voles, Mice, and Lemmings*, appears in the Old Testament. Although the vole passages are omitted from the English Bible, Elton cites the Vulgate and the Septuagint translations as telling how God sent a vole plague to punish the Philistines for carrying off the Arc of the Covenant. Unable to fight off the pests, the Philistines listened to their priests and returned the arc along with five golden mice as a gift to appease the angry god.

Concerning mice, Aristotle remarked that:

> The rate of propagation of field mice in country places, and the destruction that they cause, are beyond all telling. In many places, their number is so incalculable that but very little of the corn crop

> is left to the farmer; and so rapid is their mode of proceedings that sometimes a small farmer will one day observe that it is time for reaping, and on the following morning, when he takes his reapers afield, he finds his entire crop devoured.

In 1822, French naturalist and lawyer Charles Gérard said that his town of Alsace was completely ravaged by rodents. "It was a living and hideous scourging of the earth, which appeared perforated all over, like a sieve," he writes. The picture he paints, the devastation breaking like a wave, the "small, swift, flitting forms that infest the ground and devour all living plants," and the inhabitants' vain counterattack of fumigation, poison, plowing, trenching, and prayers is a futile one. After reading the accounts of rodent infestation, it's no surprise that Hamelin's denizens piled the Pied Piper with praise and gifts when he ridded them of their own plague. I wonder if they ever doubted that their children were worth the trade.

RIDING HIGH in a hay swather as a child with my father, I remember watching the small black flashes flee in the seconds that the blades exposed the ground. The mice, out in the open, flitted away from the machine's churning mouth and dodged the huge tires. When one would flatten out and freeze, I knew it was a goner. From the air-conditioned cab, some seventies band blaring in the background, I saw the world relieved of mice one by one.

As I looked down from the tractor or down the barrel of a rifle, death seemed inconsequential. When I shot a bird, for instance, I usually arrived at the corpse post-trauma. They were done flopping and just lay there, wings folded in like some unacceptable specimen ruined by the spot of blood wetting its chest feathers. Once the bird was still and hard, I'd retrieve it by the back legs and proudly show it off to friends or relatives. But if I arrived on the scene to see it bouncing and flapping on the forest floor or breathing its last half breath, I would spend another shell to end its misery. Only once the creature lay down and died would I dare examine the holes, the warm body, and cover it with a sheet of leaves and grass.

MY EXPERIENCE WITH MICE has been limited. The first time on the farm was in a potato cellar. Braden and I were laying out lines of aluminum ventilation tubes. Once set, the potatoes would be piled on top of them. Throughout the winter, fans blew the length of the cellar and into the tubes, circulating air to keep the crop fresh until spring.

Years before, Braden had found a discarded puppy at the corner by the gas station that he named Smoke. The dog grew into a vile animal, some type of spotted-heeler with a humped back and muscled jackal-like front legs. It ran slack-jawed and sideways and quixotic, its limp tongue hanging out its snout. Smoke found great pleasure in nipping at my ankles. Smoke became such a presence on the farm that if he wasn't in the back of Braden's pickup, I would ask why, almost as if the dog were a coworker, almost as if we had important canine tasks lined out for the day. When Smoke did show up, however, I avoided him.

But the day in the cellar, Smoke lurched behind us, watching as we rolled the tubes off the stack and down to their places. Braden and I lifted a tube from the floor, and a fat mouse scurried out from underneath. I flinched and dropped the tube on the concrete with a clang. The mouse froze at the sound. Braden yelled and pointed at the shivering rodent. In one jowl-cracking snap, Smoke had snagged, chomped, and swallowed the mouse. The dog walked to Braden, working its jaws like some appeased gator, expecting a thorough rubdown in praise.

II

MY FATHER'S MAIN FARM, up in the hills, stretched from a highway back to a reservoir that fed the valley's canals. Once the pumps and wells became available, the previous owner laid more than three miles of mainline pipe from the highway to the lake. The old tar-coated tubes, fifty years old, began to rot and crumble. A constant job for Garland, the farm mechanic, was to load up the welder, drive down the narrow farm roads, and patch the leaks. Watering was so important that even one day without it would stunt the crop's growth. From May to August, irrigation consumed the farmers' lives.

I became a teen and was rewarded with more hard work. Now my middays were spent shoveling grain bins, welding, and servicing equipment. My rifle had been locked away not to be seen again until hunting season in October.

One day in early spring, my father explained the changes that would be happening to his farm. Computerized irrigation pivots were much more efficient than handlines. If placed in the center of a square field, the new pivots spanned a quarter-mile and watered 24/7. The vibrant green hills seemed to grow these long, lethargic robots almost overnight. Neighbors bought them and soon pivots were the only way to water. My father had sent Garland out the day before with an acetylene torch to cut off all the risers which connected to the handlines. It was my job to take the backhoe and gather up all of the discarded steel pipes. Garland would then weld shut the holes, and we would never have to move pipe again.

The backhoe epitomized my father's concept of economics—unless dead, employed. Not until we had dragged some defunct machine to our farm junkyard would he talk about buying a replacement. For this reason, the backhoe lacked vital elements of comfort and safety: front windshield, door, back window, seat cushion, radio, and brakes were all nonexistent. A sparked-out screwdriver served as a key to bridge the solenoid and starter. The kill switch was a wire coat hanger wrapped around the throttle. Both operations, dangerously enough, were performed while standing in front of the driver's side tire.

Spring, and the snow banks had melted almost completely. The rusting backhoe had been winterized and parked, so Garland helped me check the fluids, clean the cab, and start the monstrosity for the first time that year. Red shreds from a paper Coke cup and newspaper covered the floor. Parked machinery made a perfect winter's nest for birds and other such pests.

While the backhoe sputtered and warmed, I went to the shop and dressed for the day. Over my T-shirt I pulled a green hooded sweatshirt, and on top of that wore a thick, wool lined denim coat. The jacket's retro collar was wide and corduroy. I wore it open at the throat—an empty hole was left at the top, the remnants of a copper button. For some reason, I had vowed to never buy work gloves, so I stole a pair of leathers from Garland that had holes in the fingertips and palms. A New York Jets winter cap was under the seat of my pickup. I put it on and walked to the backhoe, its black exhaust coughing up into the dirty sky.

Like it always does in spring, the wind roared from the east, down the river canyon and pushed out like a delta over the farm. I wound the backhoe up to 2000 rpms and wandered across the fields towards the scarred section of mainline. Garland had placed a shovel in the cab in case of getting the backhoe stuck. I propped the tool from floor to ceiling along the doorframe.

I turned into the wind, and it blasted through the windshield's empty orifice. But the wind blew enough heat from the wrapped-tight engine that I felt sweat gather along my forehead. I threw off my hat and ran a gloved hand through my dirty hair.

My job was more annoying than difficult. Stretched over a mile were the abstracted tubes, thrown out into the field every thirty feet. I would arrive at one, park the backhoe, climb out, load the four-foot pipe into the front loader bucket, climb back in, drive thirty feet, and so on. Once I had a bucketful, I'd drive to the end of the field, stack the tubes, and return.

I loaded the tubes and drove into the wind. Driving back empty, the wind whipped through the lack of a back window. I had to keep the backhoe revved high to push through the loose dirt. All of the noise combined—the wind, the engine, the constant clanging of tubes in the bucket—was deafening. I replaced my hat to cover my ears.

After the third round, I had discovered a new system. Instead of stopping when I neared a tube, I'd leave the backhoe in gear and leap from it, snatch the tube, throw it in the bucket of the moving machine, and jump back inside when the tractor ran past. By my fifth jump, I sweated profusely. Running through the dirt, heaving the steel tubes, leaping from soft ground to moving machinery was no easy feat. The wind picked up, and dirt particles blew into my eyes and glazed my sticky face with a gritty lamina. I tromped on, jumping, running, heaving. It was me, my yellow mechanical beast, and the fields, nothing else for miles.

ACCORDING TO NICHOLAS COLLIAS of the University of California, aggression in vertebrates is most frequently expressed in two forms: defense of territory, and hierarchies of precedence within social groups.

J.P. Scott, in his article "Agonistic Behavior of Mice and Rats," explains one difference between mice and rat young: "Perhaps the most fundamental of these differences is the complete absence of playful fighting in young mice." Rats seventeen days old will begin to romp and box with their peers. Mice will not. For this reason, adult mice hesitate much longer before attacking. While rats have a list of pre-attack behavior, mice have two: "mincing" (prancing about), and tail-rattling. In Scott's study, tail-rattling, or switching, is seen as a warning and threat to the opponent, similar to growling in carnivores. After switching, a mouse will strike.

I JUMPED into the backhoe and headed for the next tube. The wind pummeled me; my coat collar snapped and floated against my cheeks. Had I a button, I could have closed the coat and ridded myself of the distraction. Instead, I constantly smoothed down the thick fabric.

I threw in another tube and caught the handrail, letting the tractor's forward motion pull me up. Once I sat, my collar started snapping again. My cheeks stung from being beaten, and now an inconsistent itch warmed my nape. I flipped up the collar, hoping to tame the coat. My hands followed it around the back and found a thin string. I yanked free the string and threw it to the floor.

I caught the mouse's movement as it scurried between my feet. Its brown and white hair bristled, and its leathery tail switched back and forth.

In the milliseconds it took my nervous system to carry the message from eyeballs to brain, then spinal cord to sciatic nerves, I achieved levitation. My knees floated up past the steering wheel and stopped somewhere around my ears. In one graceful and gauche lunge, I flew through the open doorframe feet first. Like D.D. Homes, the 19th century British trickster who in obfuscated dining halls hovered above party guests and royalty, I flew through the backhoe's open door prostrate and, in my case, petrified.

When I landed in the field, I began to strip clothing. Gloves first, then denim jacket, the sweatshirt, the T-shirt, all of which I wildly flung away. Bare-chested and dripping, I rubbed my neck, my hair, slapped my biceps, and cursed in confusing strings of profanity. Had the bastard bored into my neck? Had it nested or laid its eggs?

The adrenaline hit my empty stomach. My fright changed to anger. I ran to the backhoe, which had veered out farther into the field, and from the step shifted it into neutral. With the shovel handle, I bludgeoned the fat little fink to death. Then I scraped the mouse's broken body from the floor and flung it as far as I could. The tractors would come to work the ground soon and destroy the corpse completely. Before I replaced my clothing, I shook each piece like a beach towel, ensuring the attacker had left no stragglers.

III

FAKIRS ARE INDIAN HOLY MEN who intentionally live lives of extreme poverty in order to reach a richer asceticism. They employ drastic measures of discomfort and self-mutilation to do so. They lie on beds of nails and immerse themselves for prolonged times in water and hot ash. They keep their fists clenched indefinitely, allowing their own nails to grow straight into their palms. They lie or sit in one place for years and beg for their food. All this, for spirituality.

I'm sure many go home at night after a long day of begging to a loving family and plop down in front of the boob tube to catch the latest Bollywood hack flick. Sadly, charlatans exist in every world. But I'm convinced some have truly renounced worldly wealth, put their trust in something unseen, and pursue greater light and knowledge. These disciples, unlike their fraudulent friends, they'll sleep on coals if they have to.

It has been said that the highest form of levitation is transportation. One example: Jesus walking on water. Post-Biblical texts point out that more than seventy-two Catholic saints have levitated. The power is duplicated throughout the world: wizards of savage tribes, mystics in the East, and hoards of David Blains have achieved this blatant defiance of gravity. Fakirs, too, strive for levitation, and many have been transported to that elevation. Could this be the drive that inspired Icarus and the Wright Brothers? Does the same force make men farm the hills or construct impressive houses in high places?

AFTER I GRADUATED with my bachelor's degree, I returned to the farm to work. My father conned me into it; a new venture, bright futures. The year before, he and two other business partners undertook a new cash crop, Kentucky blue grass. A sod farm. My father, functioning as the farmer-in-residence, supplied the machinery and manpower. A plastic surgeon offered his eighty acres. The man who'd landscaped the surgeon's yard became the manager. Within the first year, the landscaper left the venture for different pursuits. Too busy to operate the farm himself, my father talked me into running it before I left for Arizona. At twenty-three, I'd decided to leave the farming life for more scholarly pursuits, perhaps encouraged by the six-dollar-an-hour wage I'd made up until then.

We had rented the ground before the surgeon had bought it, so I was familiar with the watering system. Thinking the sod business would take off without any hang-ups, the trio had purchased top-of-the-line equipment, including a new irrigation pivot. The control panel for it sat right off the highway. The view from the concrete pivot pad was beautiful. The land stayed flat for two hundred yards and then dropped down to a box-valley filled with wheat and hay. The last manager had started harvesting in the back, so the grass butted against the pivot pad. Once summer hit, it was a sea of emerald green back-dropped by ragged cliffs and a mountain road that led northeast to Kelly's Canyon and the Snake.

The sod farm proved to be my first real stake in the family business, and even though I was leaving, I wanted to do well. After graduation, I spent my waking hours on that hill of grass, investigating, planning, and predicting the future. While my father worried in hundredweight scales and worked the ground with forty-foot implements, I employed micro-management. I sold sod by the square foot and ensured that each foot was as perfect as I could get it. I shepherded the small farm from morning light to sundown.

The winter had caused many problems. Snowfall was higher than usual, and melt-off took additional time, which resulted in a drastic spurt of the rodent population. They flourished under the snow pack. Once the snow retreated, the animals were vibrant and healthy. That summer, my father said that when he walked across the potato rows, he could feel their tunnels collapse underfoot. The rodents destroyed at least ten percent of the crops. The surplus of mice brought additional hawks and burrowing owls to feed. The birds fought for roosting space on the power poles. During the squabbles, a weak one would fall into the lines and short out the power which would stop the irrigation system. The birds died, as did the plants and mice.

I faced similar obstacles. The mice had made a chain of tunnels that stretched the length of the sod field. This caused two problems. To harvest, the ground had to be as level as possible. The mice tunnels caved in everything and caused the pieces of grass to break and crumble. The second was dealing with customers. Who wanted a lawn that looked like swiss cheese?

I remedied the section as best I could with an old pavement roller Pops had bought at a farm auction for fifty bucks. I traversed the farm for two days straight, the wide machine mashing down the ground. From my high view, I could see the mice scampering for safety when I roared over top their nests. They were everywhere. The barrel-sized pump had holes along the turbine to allow air flow to cool the shaft. After I had oiled and prepped the pump, I pushed the green button to start it. The turbine spun, and a nest of weeds and garbage poofed out and floated to the ground. After ignition, a baby mouse lay shaking by the pump until its life faded out of its body. Perhaps that tiny pink mouse changed something in me. Barehanded, I picked it up by its tail and dropped it into a hole, a burial of sorts.

The grass grew, business prospered, and the hills supported the new crop nicely. I avoided harvesting among the mice's territory—the sod rolls crumbled when we stacked them on the pallets. By the end of summer, I'd sold everything but the strips of mouse grass. We had to harvest that, too. It took us hours to take the shoddy stuff, but we did it and were done.

An irrigation pivot creates its own tire tracks each year by moving back and forth along its own path, wetting the ground and pushing its tall cleated tires forward. By mid-summer, the tracks are three- or four-feet deep in places, and the pivot will get itself stuck or high-centered. Because overwatering is just as detrimental as not watering at all, making sure the pivot ran smoothly and consistently worried me—the mode of transport for the water had changed since the settlers, but the pressure to keep it running had not.

When we harvested the mouse-infested grass, we ended up throwing off more scraps than we actually sold. My last job was to clean off the scraps. I carried them to the pivot tracks and threw them into the deep spots, hoping the additions would keep the pivot's A-beam from dragging the whole contraption to a standstill.

It was one night in the gloaming that I picked up a small piece of sod and touched a field mouse that hid underneath. I jumped back and swore. The mouse hunched up and froze. We stayed deadlocked for what felt like a full minute. I knew Braden or Garland or my father would have no problem stomping the pest. Smoke would snarf it down without a second thought.

But I couldn't do it. Its small form shivered as the day moved to night, and in that retreating light, I examined its tan body, its white little feet. I noticed my own dirt-stained knees, the mud that had accumulated in the crooks of my elbows, the soil that glazed my armhairs and palms and fingertips. The mouse's coat could not be better colored for its life of digging, scampering, surviving. Its whiskers twitched, the mouse sniffing the air. I smelled the same moisture as the pivot pumped water behind us, fooling me to memories of summer thunderstorms and canal swimming.

But I couldn't let the mouse run away. Goliathing above it, I surged out a clumsy kick. In the time that my leg cocked back and then struck, I decided not to kill it but instead scoot the thing through the air and out of sight for good.

The problem, I think, with immature boys is their lack of comprehension. I'd killed hundreds of animals because I failed to acknowledge the strength of molded lead propelled by potassium nitrate and sulfur. As a maturing man, I blanked on the force that my leg carried and kicked the mouse too hard.

Its body flew end over end a few feet and plunked onto the bare dirt. I crouched in front of the injured animal. Blood spotted its yellow teeth, and its front paws boxed the air. It breathed laboredly and shallow.

I was too scared to pick it up; I didn't want its blood on my hands. I pulled it onto an oddly shaped piece of sod, its brown body offset drastically by the greenness of the grass. I set the mouse and sod in the bottom of the pivot's muddy path, knowing that in four or five hours, the tons of steel that carried the water would churn the mouse back underground. I walked off towards the pickup, leaving for the day.

But I returned—my actions deserved no easy reconciliation—and placed a heavy foot on the upturned sod and lowered my weight onto it. Beneath me, the mouse deflated and expired. When I stepped out of the track, sadness surged through my body so completely that my limbs tingled. Goosebumps appeared and disappeared in places they never had, across my lower abdomen, the backs of my knees. I looked down, imagining what had occurred on the underside of the heart-shaped sod. As darkness overtook the hill, I looked down. Grass licked around my boots, and, for a split-second, it felt like I was floating.

Prodigal Son

JAMES GOLDBERG

FROM *The New Play Project*

(In the darkness.)

SON: Scene one. First encounters.

(Lights up.)

SON: I first heard of the Church when I was a kid. We went to visit my grandparents in Salt Lake and they took us to visit what I initially assumed was just a really big, stony church. Or maybe a castle?

The next encounter I had with the church was substantially more—(CHRISTY enters.) aesthetically pleasing. In one of the most courageous acts of my life to that point, I had actually found a moment alone with Christy and asked her if she wanted to go out with me that Sunday. And she just looked at me. I mean really just—wow. I probably could have picked up a car at the time if she'd asked me to, there was so much adrenaline pumping through my veins. But she didn't. All she said was:

(Lights shift.)

CHRISTY: I can't. (Beat. He's crushed.) I mean, not Sunday. It's just...I'm Mormon, and so Sundays I can't...What are you doing tomorrow?

SON: What was I doing—? Like it mattered what else I had planned? (Back to her.) Tomorrow's good. (To audience.) Saturday, as it turned out, went miraculously well, enough to turn into some other days, and before too long it was... (Crosses to her; covers her eyes.) What're you doing tonight?

CHRISTY (smiling): I can't. It's Monday.

SON: Are you Jewish, too, or something?

CHRISTY: No...that's Friday nights. Mondays I'm definitely Mormon. There's this thing we do called family home evening, so...

SON: Right.

CHRISTY: Do you want to just come?

SON: Umm... (To audience.) Put yourself in my position. Christy or no Christy...two Sabbaths? This was sounding more and more like the kind of cult you're trained to expect. (To CHRISTY.) I don't think—.

CHRISTY: C'mon, it'll be fun.

SON: And then she smiled, so I was pretty much doomed. Ended up talking to her dad afterwards til like 11:50 about everything remotely gospel-esque that you can possibly imagine. Looking back, I misunderstood 90% of the things he said, but I came home with a Book of Mormon *and* a Bible hidden in my backpack. You've got to understand, Christy's dad is as notoriously thorough as her family is notoriously late.

My dad never gave me a curfew or anything, but midnight's not exactly typical for me to be wandering in on a Monday night...he was still up when I came in, though I doubt he ever would have admitted to waiting.

DAD: Hey.

SON: Hey.

DAD: How was school?

SON: Good, good.

DAD: Get a lot of studying done?

SON: I was out with Christy.

DAD: Ah. OK, that makes sense. You gonna bring her over sometime, or is it not that—.

SON: We'll see. I'll try.

DAD: Whatever. No pressure.

SON: Thanks. (Heads up to his room.)

DAD: Daniel?

SON: Yeah?

DAD: Just...remember rule number two, OK? I know you're a good kid, just...remember.

(Lights change.)

SON: OK. Stop there. This probably isn't making sense. You need to know that we have two rules in my family. That's important. The first is, "Take care of your feet." And I do. The second goes: "Don't do anything stupid." Sometimes my dad finishes the quote and says, "Like getting yourself killed," but usually he just sticks to the, "Don't do anything stupid," part. I don't know exactly what he was referring to when he brought it up that night, maybe reminding me not to get anyone pregnant, but I almost wondered if he knew. Knew that thanks to Christy Chang, I was about to start investigating the religion he'd left in his youth. And that, thanks to Christy Chang's father, I felt distinctly like I was smuggling contraband into the house.

(Lights out.)

DAD: Scene two. Bad news.

(Lights up.)

CHRISTY: Hey. Does your dad know they're coming?

SON: Yeah.

CHRISTY: And he's OK with that?

SON: He respects me.

CHRISTY: Where is he?

SON: He's not staying. He told me to call when we're through and he'll come home.

CHRISTY: If he feels that way—we could have had the discussion at my house.

SON: What, you were hoping he'd stay and listen?

CHRISTY: Well, yeah…I mean your dad's a great guy. And how cool would it be if—.

SON: Christy. You don't know my dad. This is the last required discussion, right? I mean, I'm ready after this?

(Lights out. Spot up on DAD elsewhere.)

SON (to audience): When I told my dad I wanted to get baptized…it was like something went out in his eyes. I'd already told him I was investigating, so I'd seen him angry. And he'd found out that Christy was a member, and I'd been hiding that from him, so I'd seen him disappointed. But I'd never seen him—.

We'd fought about it, a lot. By the time I got baptized, I knew more about the dark side of Church history than most people learn in their lives, like—.

DAD: Some of those things he talks about as a background to the first vision didn't happen until 1822 or '23. Think, Daniel, why would he lie about the year it happened unless he was making stuff up?

SON: Or—.

DAD: It's very convenient of Mr. Chang to say that racism is only in the Church's past, but it's also right in their scriptures…unless they've edited even more out since the last time I read them.

SON: Or—.

DAD: She honestly told you she thought polygamy started with Brigham Young? If anything, he toned it down! Let me tell you about Joseph—.

SON: And every time he'd ask—.

DAD: You're a smart, boy, Daniel. I didn't raise you to—. Why are you still doing this?

SON: All I could say was: they told me I would feel some kind of gentle, comfortable feeling or a still, small voice or something. But when I started reading and praying and stuff, it was more like— Like there was something standing right in the room. I wasn't expecting that, you know, so I don't see how I could have been making it up. And then came this feeling like fire, Dad, not like soft happy feelings but like Elijah-calling-it-down-from-heaven kind of fire. Like our-God-is-a-consuming-fire kind of fire. How can I not believe it when I've felt that? It's not about Christ;, it's not something I can just think through; it's—.

DAD: Yeah. Yeah, I get it. The fire of the Spirit. Look, I don't know what that really is, but I've felt it, too. I've felt it, and guess what? In the end, it just leaves you feeling burned out.

SON (to audience): I couldn't tell it to him, then, but…all my life. I'd been waiting for something, you know? And I never knew what. But I'd have these feeling sometimes like when I went to my friend's Bar Mitzvah, and it was like God was driving by on a train but there weren't any scheduled stops to pick me up. And maybe I could have run, maybe I could have jumped up there in front of everybody and said, "Hey, can it be my turn now? I know I'm not Jewish, but…just Bar Mitzvah me, OK?"

But, you know, obviously I didn't. And the train went on by. Until I felt fire from heaven reading the Book of Mormon. And even though my dad talked me through it 'til I knew in my mind it couldn't be historically true, even though he told me all the ways the institutional church was going to use and twist me if I joined—.

I figured, if God's a train, and fate didn't leave me any stops…maybe I've gotta stand on the tracks. I can't get on smoothly like everybody else, but if I take that step out onto those tracks, then God'll have to hit me. And I'll know then whatever it is the prophets and saints used to know. (Pause.)

So on November 9th, 2005, I told him. The light went out in his eyes, his face fell just a little, and then he said:

(Lights change.)

DAD: You're eighteen.

SON (in the scene now, to DAD): So the answer's yes?

DAD: The answer is you're eighteen. I don't get a say in it.

SON: Dad, I don't want to hurt you.

DAD: And I don't want you to get hurt, but you haven't been exactly open to that message, so...

SON: So?

DAD: So you're eighteen.

(Pause. DAD turns to exit.)

SON: That's it?

DAD: That's it. (Pause.)

SON: Are you gonna come?

DAD: No.

SON: I don't want...I mean, it'd be nice to have family there, you know?

DAD: If your mom were alive, she could probably handle it. I can't. OK? (Exiting.) You can do whatever the hell you want, but just leave me alone.

(Dark.)

SON: Scene three. Distance.

(Lights up on DAD.)

DAD: We're far too casual, I think, in the way we talk about losing. "I've lost my keys," for example, really means you've mislaid them. We say we're "lost" when we're just disoriented. And we "lose" our tempers all the time, only to find them again a few minutes later—. (Pause. Deep breath.)

I wish we wouldn't dilute the best word we have for when things are truly and permanently gone. "Lost cause" is a good phrase. It's a cold, hard dose of reality. No one goes out to find a lost cause. It's just lost. That phrase understands the power of the word's finality.

It's a finality we need. When you lose a game...after the clock has ticked away all 48 minutes of sweat and adrenaline, when that last-second three-ball bounces off the rim: victory isn't just missing somewhere, waiting to be rediscovered between the couch cushions. It's over. An opportunity is gone, and there's a certain comfort to the clinical finality of the word "lost." The word helps you accept a thing which you have no possible ability to change.

So when I tell you that a long time ago I lost my faith, I don't want you to imagine that I've misplaced it or that I could be capable of finding it again. Lost faith is like a lost limb...if it's broken and bleeding, if you try to patch it up and it ends up inflamed and infected...at some point you have to cut it off. And after you've lost it, the only thing left is the occasional flash of phantom pain.

I lost my faith. Twenty years later, I lost my wife. And now maybe I'm losing my son.

Don't take away from the only word I have to cope with all that.

(Lights out.)
(Pause.)
(Fade in.)

SON: Being just the two of us. I mean, since mom died. We were close, my dad and I. You know a lot of people felt sorry for me, not having a mom, and yeah, I missed her, but how many sons get to hang out with their dads so much? We'd do something almost every weekend. But now, Sunday afternoons go:

DAD: Hey

SON: Hey. (Long pause. Directly to audience.) You know, it used to be I felt alone a lot. Hated malls, the way all the people wander past like zombies, so you can hardly tell where the people end and where their reflections in the storefronts start. There were days I felt like I was stuck in some weird sci-fi movie where I'm the last man on earth, but it's a thousand times worse because there are all these empty bodies still wandering through the mall. And the only thing on earth I have to identify with is a print I see in a storefront of that famous painting with the scream.

But then, I found out that we're all children of God. And suddenly, it was like everywhere I go I'm surrounded by shimmering hidden pools of light. When God is everywhere, and his children are everywhere, how could I ever feel alone? (Pause.) Except at home.

It's like my life is an inverted photograph. Everything that used to be hard is easy, and everything that used to be easy is hard.

Knowing I have a Father in Heaven, I feel for the first time like I could be just fine going anywhere in the world. But it can be so lonely Sunday afternoons.

(Lights out.)

CHRISTY: Scene four. Decisions. (Lights up.) You're not even gonna apply?

SON: No. (Beat.) Is that a problem?

CHRISTY: No, no, it's cool…it's just I always kind of assumed I'd end up going to BYU.

SON: So go.

CHRISTY: …

SON: What?

CHRISTY: …

SON: You wanted to go to school the same place?

CHRISTY: I know it's probably stupid to be worrying about, but…yeah. Yes. I did. Do…

SON: There are phones. And we both have gmail accounts, which is practically like living together—.

CHRISTY (holding him): That is so not the same.

SON: I don't know…I keep waiting for the bishop to ask if I've been cohabiting with anyone on chat. My palms get so sweaty at the end of the interview I have to make up excuses to avoid shaking hands—. (She kisses him. Beat.) You're right. It's not the same.

CHRISTY: See. (Pause.)

SON: Christy?

CHRISTY: Hm?

SON: I want to go on a mission. (She smiles.) Maybe you were already taking that for granted, but I didn't grow up with it, so I really had to think it out. I'm gonna put in my papers early enough to leave next summer. That's why I don't want to risk a

BYU acceptance letter showing up in the mail. I'm probably gonna stay home and go to OSU. (Beat.) I can't stand to make my dad think I'm leaving him twice.

(Lights change.)

DAD: OSU's a good school. Well, it's a big school, and statistically speaking, any school that's big enough ends up accidentally good at something. (Beat.) You sure that's what you want?

SON: Yeah.

DAD: I saw the acceptance letter from Northwestern. Don't tell me that was your safety school.

SON: Well, I'd have to go somewhere if Ohio State didn't let me in. (Beat.)

DAD: This doesn't have anything to do with Christy, does it? You're not staying for her?

SON: She's not staying. She'll be going to BYU.

DAD: Ah. Yes, of course.

SON (to audience): Looking back, I probably should have told him then. But "I want to stay at home with you" just didn't seem like it would go over well with "because next year I'm leaving on a mission" tacked on to the end of it. So I told him a half-truth instead. (Back to DAD.)

It's simple economics, Dad. Northwestern may be a better school, but does the increased marginal utility justify the costs? Not only is OSU cheaper, I've got a scholarship, I can live at home—.

DAD (laughing): Well, I'm glad you've got something to show for all that studying in AP Econ. But you've got to take into account that education isn't just an expense. It's an investment. (Brief pause.) Why do you think your mom and I decided to match every dollar you put in your savings account with five? That money's for your education. You might as well use it.

SON (to audience): I probably should have told him. I probably should have told him then. But: (Back.) Dad, (To audience.) I said, and this was the truth, (Back.) Where else am I gonna buy the quality of tutoring I'm going to be able to get right here for free?

DAD (sighs): Just remember that flattery is not going to win you every argument in your life…even if it's winning you this one, OK?

SON: OK.

(Fade out.)

CHRISTY: Scene five.

ALL: Goodbyes.

(Lights up.)

SON: Sunscreen? Did you remember that? I've heard that out West the sun does actually shine in the fall. That might just be some kind of urban legend—.

CHRISTY: I've got sunscreen. I've got everything.

SON: OK.

CHRISTY: OK.

SON: Just watch out for all the hot Mormon guys out there, all right?

CHRISTY: There really aren't that many unless you convert them. (Beat.) Dan?

SON: Yeah?

CHRISTY: I want to give something to your dad, before I go. But I thought I'd better ask you first.

SON: What? What is it?

CHRISTY: I wrote my testimony in a Book of Mormon. I know you think it's a long shot, but I want to give it to him. Even if it doesn't make a difference. Even if he never reads—.

SON: He's read it, Christy.

CHRISTY: Yeah, I know. So have I, but it's always different if you read it again. And he's a really bright guy. Maybe this time he'll see—.

SON: I don't want to talk about it. Do what you think is right.

CHRISTY: It can't really be wrong, can it? (Beat.)

SON: I don't think you realize how much the Book of Mormon is God's middle finger to anyone that proud of his intellect.

(Lights change. CHRISTY hands DAD
the Book of Mormon as SON speaks.)

SON (cont.): She gave it to him. Last thing she did before her dad drove her to the airport. He just took it and nodded. After she was gone…he waited until the car was all the way out of sight before he turned to me:

DAD: She's a nice girl, Daniel. And I'm not going to hold this against her. But if you end up married to a Latter-day Saint, (Beat.) just make sure she understands I have boundaries. All right? (Hands book to SON.)

SON: I nod, and I try not to let my jaw set in an inherited stubbornness. There's a knot in my stomach now. I've developed a whole tangle of them over the past year.

(Lights shift.)

DAD: I try to always be the kind of person who logically thinks things through. I think there'd be a lot less pain in the world if more people would just do that. I try to be objective about things; I try to be honest with myself.

But I still held out that elusive glimmer of hope that maybe the whole thing would be over after she left. That their relationship would fizzle out and maybe his new religion with it.

He's not in it for her, though. Too bad, but it's true. And I'm not about to start now pretending things are different than they are just because that's the way I want them. (Beat.)

Things get better, though, with Daniel in college. He's taking an incredible course load, doing things I never would have dared as a freshman, and we'll work through tough material together, sometimes stuff I haven't thought about in years, sometimes theories that are as new and intriguing to me as they are to him. I haven't felt this way since Danny was a little kid and I was teaching him the constellations. We'd be out camping, memorizing the night sky, and he started asking questions about why you can see different stars in different seasons, and how stars burn, and pretty soon I'm talking this nine-year-old kid through the raw power of hydrogen fusion and—I never thought I'd feel that way again.

But he's young again, and his mind is so hungry, and even

though I still can't get over the way he leaves every Sunday morning, we end up staying up way too late talking about life, the universe, and everything Sunday nights.

I feel so exhausted one Monday morning I end up being late to work for the first time in a long time. And that night—.

I'm always a little annoyed Monday nights because instead of studying like he should be, he insists on going to a student FHE. If he wants to spend his weekend at church, fine. Institute Thursday nights…whatever, you know? At least he's not at the bar drinking.

But c'mon, a bunch of college students getting together to hold a fake family home evening? Doesn't that seem just a little wrong to you? How many hours of social pressure and indoctrination do you need before it's enough? I've got no problem with family time, but those kids aren't a family!

I'm sorry. I'm just making excuses for myself. What is done is done. What happened that night happened. I can't change it, but at least I can accept responsibility.

(Lights add to reveal son entering.)

SON (like a child): Dad?

DAD (still to audience): That tone probably isn't accurate, but in my memory, he sounds like a kid again. Like he's getting up from bed to ask for a drink of water.

SON (regular tone): Dad, we need to talk.

DAD: Or like he's waking up from a very bad dream.

SON (like a kid): Dad!

DAD: What? What is it?

SON (back to normal): Nothing much, it's just… (Beat.) Let me start over again, OK?

DAD: Is something wrong?

SON: No, no. (Beat. Deep breath.) I just thought I should tell you—
Yesterday I put in my papers. To go on a mission.

(Beat.)

(Beat.)

(Beat.)

(Long pause.)

DAD: You did what?

SON: I'm going on a mission, Dad.

(Beat.)

DAD: How you gonna pay for that?

SON: I've got plenty of money in the bank. I've been on a full ride scholarship; even my textbooks have been covered.

DAD: That money was for your education.

SON: The way I see it, that's part of what a mission is.

DAD: No. No, not in my eyes. I can't believe you turned down Northwestern to go on a—.

SON: I stayed home because I wanted time with you.

DAD: Oh? That's supposed to make me feel better, is it? 'Cause right about now I'm feeling just great.

SON: Dad.

DAD: That is not the way you're going to use that money.

SON: It's my bank account. You guys helped, but it's based on my savings from my jobs; it's in my name—.

DAD: You think you're gonna remember all the things you've been studying after two years of not being allowed to touch a textbook?

SON: Missionaries get blessed, the Lord will help—.

DAD: Half of them don't even remember how to speak English when they get home! How are you possibly going to retain all your organic chemistry?

SON: There are more important things in life than O-Chem. (Pause.)

DAD: Everything I have given you, you've turned your back on...do you realize that? I taught you to value your intellect, I taught you to work toward your potential...I taught you to have some pride, and I never once told you that's a sin! Sometimes pride is the only thing you've got. That was my gift to you. That was your inheritance! And now you want to throw it all away: your intellect, your independence, everything.

SON: Dad, I—.

DAD: I am not going to let you throw away your mother's money.
SON: She's dead! And since you don't believe in a life after death, I don't see how you can claim to know how she would want me to use it.
DAD: SHUT UP! Just…shut up, and go to your room. (Beat.)
SON: I'm not five years old. (Beat.) Wow…this is—. I honestly don't think you've told me to go to my room since I was five. I'm an adult, Dad, you can't tell me to go to my room just because you don't agree with a decision I've made.
DAD: You're right. I can't. If you don't want to go to your room, then you can get out of my house and go be an adult on your own.

(Lights out.)

SON: Scene six. Isolation. (Lights up on DAD.) I'll never know if he really meant that, because I didn't stay to find out. My friend Pratap lived in the dorms, and he'd already been through three roommates. The first dropped out three weeks into classes and went home. Pratap had the room to himself for the rest of the first quarter. His second-quarter roommate turned out to be dealing a fairly impressive volume of cocaine out of the closet…after a midnight FBI raid, he dropped out, too…and went to jail. No one really knows what happened to Pratap's third roommate. He just kind of disappeared, didn't even take his stuff with him. We used to joke that Pratap had gotten so used to having a single he'd wired a powerful electrode to the bottom of the other bed and disposed of the body quietly one night. It was hard to imagine Pratap killing someone, of course, but had he decided to, he was certainly discreet enough to have gotten away with it.

It was that combination of factors—the free bed and knowing that I wouldn't be asked questions—that made me decide to take two bags and walk all the way down to Pratap's that night. I didn't want to talk to anyone for a while. Anyone but God, at least.

(Lights out. A phone rings.
Lights come half up on a separate area.)

DAD (into phone): Hello?

CHRISTY (somewhat distressed): Hi, Mr. Pratt, sorry to be calling so late, but I really need to talk to Daniel and he's not answering his phone.

DAD: OK…I'll go get him.

CHRISTY: I'm really sorry.

DAD: No, it's fine. I understand. (DAD exits. A moment passes. DAD reenters.) Christy?

CHRISTY: Yeah?

DAD: I'm afraid he isn't here right now.

(Lights go down. Up again, different.)

SON: I called the next day while he was at work and left a message. Hey, Dad, it's me…I'm sorry for how things went last night. Just wanted to let you know I'm fine, now, staying with a friend, still going to classes and everything, so there's nothing to worry about. OK. Umm…bye. I'll talk to you later.

He called back a couple times but didn't leave a message. I finally answered two days later, and he said

DAD: Hey.

SON: Hey.

DAD: How are classes?

SON: Good. Good.

DAD: That's really good. I—. You know, I'm still here. If you need help studying or anything.

SON: That's good to know.

DAD: Good.

SON: I didn't really like to talk to Christy about my dad. At least, it always came out wrong when I tried to talk about my dad and religion, and I wasn't up to that the week I left, so I hadn't talked to her since Sunday, hadn't even listened to her messages. I called her back on Friday.

CHRISTY: Hi…

SON: Hi. (Pause.) You left some messages, and I haven't listened to them yet, but I thought I should call you back.

CHRISTY: Are you OK?

SON: I'm fine. I mean, obviously not completely fine, but…what were you calling about?

CHRISTY: I was just having a really hard time this week, but it's really not important.

SON: What's wrong? Sorry I—.

CHRISTY: I'm fine. Did something happen between you and your dad?

SON: It's not a big deal, it's just—.

(Lights shift.)

SON: And then I sobbed. For what felt like hours. Not like while telling her anything, I just sobbed. Every so often I'd start taking deep breaths instead, and I'd get control of it and I'd say about three words in as detached and analytical a way as possible, but then I'd just start sobbing again. I lay down on Pratap's extra bed without a thought as to what all that water might do if it seeped down to the hidden fatal electrode he'd been kind enough not to activate, and I sobbed until I fell asleep.

Maybe someday I'll ask her how long she stayed on the line after I settled down into measured, unconscious breaths. Maybe at some point, I started to snore and she realized that her role that night as a comforter had ended.

Maybe crying does make things a little better after all. We didn't talk about it after that night…not me and Christy, not me and my dad…but I started to call home more and then spend time there, and even though I was still sleeping at Pratap's for the rest of the school year, home was once again almost my home.

Which I should be thankful for, really, but when you've had the honest-to-goodness feeling of home, "almost" gets difficult to settle for.

(Lights shift.)

CHRISTY: When I got home that summer, he was already gone. He'd landed an internship with NASA down in Florida, which is really prestigious, right? And more importantly, seems like the kind of thing he would really enjoy...but I couldn't help feeling like he was just running from something. (Light up on DAD in another area. She talks to him.) So…everything you'd dreamed of?

SON: I don't know…I'm way too tired to dream lately. Nights it's like…eyes close, alarm rings, eyes open.

CHRISTY: They work you pretty hard, huh?

SON: Yeah. (Pause.)

CHRISTY: I saw your dad the other day at the store—.

SON (seeing a co-worker): Hey, I've gotta go. I'll call you back later.

(Lights shift back.)

CHRISTY: Look, I know I don't understand what's going on between them, and I know that maybe I can't. But it's hard to feel so shut out of such an important part of his life. I'm used to knowing him, used to being allowed to feel out who he is and where he stands. But somewhere there's a tall wall, and all I ever get out of it are stubborn looks, cryptic statements, and that one time a flood of tears.

But there's no gate, and I'm not a battering-ram kind of girl, so I have to just wait. Or else find a way around, like maybe figure out the father enough to understand the son. (Lights up on Dad in separate area. He is sorting through mail.) Hi, Mr. Pratt.

DAD: Oh. Hello, Ms. Chang. What can I do for you?

CHRISTY: I took a folklore class last semester and liked it a lot, so I volunteered to do some collection work over the summer from the professor. She's interested in gathering stories from people who were raised in the West and moved East. You're from out West, right?

DAD: That's correct.

CHRISTY: So could I interview you?

DAD: Sure. Not a problem. I'm free—. (Gets to a certain envelope and stops. Pause.)

CHRISTY: Mr. Pratt?

DAD: Sorry, Christy. You were saying?

CHRISTY: Oh…my schedule's totally flexible. When would be a good time—.

DAD: Could I call you back later about that, actually? Something came up, and I can't think of my schedule right now.

CHRISTY: OK.

DAD: Thanks.

(Lights fade out on CHRISTY, and DAD writes a forwarding address on the envelope and takes a deep breath. Lights fade out on DAD, in on SON.)

SON: I tried to make sure they sent my call to my Florida address but they screwed up and sent it home. My dad forwarded it to me unopened. It took a while to tell him where I was going because he never asked.

(Dark.)

CHRISTY: Scene seven—.

DAD: Gone.

(Lights up.)

DAD: He came home for about a week from his internship, and then he was on a plane to the MTC. Two months later, he was in Thailand, but he might as well have been up there in space along with the probe he'd spent the summer working on.

I'd stare at the stars some nights and wonder what happened to him. What it was in his genetics or environment that let things turn out this way. I tried to remember how you think when you're out there in the distant universe of faith. Sometimes I wondered if I'd done something wrong that set him up to start thinking like that.

After all, if you don't raise your kids with a religion, our language treats that like a zero. If he'd been Catholic, people would acknowledge that; they'd say he converted from Catholicism, but the way it is, they'll just think of him "joining the Church." They'll ask what he "was" before, and he'll say "Nothing." I was nothing. (Beat.)

People think that if you don't have faith in God you don't believe in anything, but that isn't true. Reality is the doctrine I raised him on. Truth trumps hope in my religion, but I'm capable of staring the universe in the face instead of having to squint at it until it fits my expectations.

My doctrine is what's real, and my only commandment is the Hippocratic oath: "Do no harm." (Beat.)

I read his letters, and as I start to write back, weighing the truth against his feelings, I realize my religion's as impossible to keep as any.

(Lights out. Lights shift.)

CHRISTY: What's a mission like?

SON: ...Christy asks me in a letter. We broke up before I left—my idea. I told her I wanted to focus on the mission, and I didn't want her to feel like she had to wait—but we do still write.

I resist the temptation to tell her it's like beating your head against a wall until one or the other gives out.

I'm really just frustrated with Thai, actually. The grammar is so simple, and the spelling is completely phonetic but—they don't put any spaces between words.

No one told me anything that could have prepared me for dealing with that. I'm used to being smart enough to deal with most things, but what do you do when your scriptures become a long stream of uninterrupted letters staring up at you and refusing to surrender their meaning to the uninitiated? My companion tells me that reading gets pretty easy once you have a decent Thai vocabulary. The words start just jumping out to you, and it all makes sense again. "Great," I think. And until then, reading scriptures is mostly just an out-of-order review of the Thai alphabet.

I find myself longing for a Urim and Thummim.

And then one night I'm so tired I can barely keep my eyes open, and all the characters seem particularly foreign and blurred, but I crack open my Thai Book of Mormon to the title page anyway. It's even more hopeless than usual, and I realize that the only thing on the whole page that makes any sense is "Jesus Christ, the Son of God." (Long pause.)

In the beginning, there was the Word, you know?

But if you don't accept the part of your mind or soul that can recognize words on tired nights, all you've got is the rational emptiness of an endless string of uninterrupted Thai letters. (Beat.)

In the week leading up to Christmas, I work up the nerve to try and explain what I think about Thai letters and the Spirit to my dad. But when I call, the phone just rings and rings. I try twelve times but he never picks up.

(Blackout.)

SON: Scene eight. Space

(Lights up.)

DAD: I know what you're thinking. You're thinking I'm too harsh, or that I don't love him, or maybe that I'm being manipulative. But don't blame me for not answering the phone.

I told you that my doctrine is what's real. How could I stand, after not having heard his voice for five months, to make chit-chat and be fake with him?

The only thing more agonizing than not communicating is pretending that you are.

(Lights shift.)

SON: How do you deal with that? You tell me: how do you deal with a father who isn't even willing to talk to you?

I know that it's true. I know that the gospel is true. If I could change that, if I could make the world into the world he believes in, maybe I would. Maybe I would, even though it's a worse world, just to have him back again. But I can't! Doesn't he realize that? There's no way to change what I know, what I've felt, what has happened to me, what I am to make things fine again. Doesn't he—.

"Forget yourself and go to work." Brother Chang gave that to me on a bookmark. And in the rural part of the country where I'm serving, where even the air is Buddhist, it's so easy to do just that. To forget all your individual drives and attachments and become no more or less than a breathing act of devotion for a while. For months, I just work. Very hard, my mission president tells me later, but it isn't hard to do. For five months, my life is like that scripture backward: knowing no joy because I'm tired of feeling pain, dangling somewhere between sense and insensibility. In May, I call home because that's what I've been told to do. I am only going through the motions, but—.

DAD: Hello?

SON: Hi.

DAD: Oh—it's... What's wrong? You're not hurt, are you?

SON: No.

DAD: You didn't do something wrong, did you?

SON: No.

DAD: They're not sending you home?

SON: No. (Beat.)

DAD: Well then why are you—.

SON: It's Mother's Day, Dad. (DAD laughs.) And he laughs. Which puzzles me until I realize that the real reason I'm supposed to be calling is to say something nice to my mother.

DAD: Wow! You've gotta love unbending institutional adherence to meaningless bureaucratic—. It's still good to hear from you. (Pause. Shift in tone.) She always loved this time of year, your mom. I don't know if you remember that.

SON: No, not really.

DAD: You were too young to really notice, I guess. Winters were hard on her, but as soon as she'd catch the scent of spring, she was a whole different person. And when all the flowers I'd planted in the garden really started coming in...I think it was in May, actually, that we first agreed on the idea of having you. But you've probably already done that math...

SON: My companion called his family before I did. He's got seven siblings, plus his grandparents were there, so he got to talk to each person for like five minutes. We have an hour to ourselves. After fifty-eight minutes, we are still going strong—.

DAD: What's Thai weather like?

SON: Hot and soggy. Depends on the time of year...the wet season is soggy; the "cool" season is hot; and the hot season is hot and soggy. It's hot and soggy now, but pretty soon we'll be back to three or four months of unbelievably soggy again.

DAD: Just...take care of your feet, OK?

SON (to audience): I decide after minute fifty-nine that I deserve an extra hour to make up for Christmas.

DAD: She always complained about how the greeting card industry had invented 80% of American holidays, but I think she accepted Mothers' Day that last year, after the picture you gave her.

SON: I don't remember—.

DAD: Yeah, your teacher had you guys draw pictures for Mothers' Day. And your mom liked it so much she kept it up for...I guess it was the rest of her life, now that I think about it.

SON: What'd I draw?

DAD: Fossils, mostly. I think that's what impressed her about it. You had your six-year-old scrawling of "Dear Mom, I love you" with the "you" landed right next to a fairly well-rendered archaeopteryx skeleton. The end of her youth, she told me. Her son had not wasted any time in seeing her as a fossil.

SON: Wow.

DAD: She'd known that day was coming; she just hadn't realized you would love fossils so much...

SON (to audience): We get to the two-hour mark...but I don't hang up. I am meticulously, almost obnoxiously obedient even as missionaries go, but I stay on the line. Pretty soon I find myself asking things like—. (Back to DAD.) How'd you know you wanted to marry her?

DAD: Because I was lucky.

SON: What does that mean?

DAD: I could talk to her. I mean really talk, about almost anything.

SON: And that was it?

DAD: Well, there was also the intense physical attraction thing, but you probably aren't as interested in that.

SON: I mean, you could talk to her, so you just knew?

DAD: You don't know how we talked. It's a miracle to be able to talk like that. (Beat.) And since I don't usually believe in miracles, I wasn't prepared to let mine go.

SON: You still miss her?

DAD: Yes. Always. (Silence.)

SON (after a moment, to audience): I wish I could keep talking for days, but we are on almost exactly opposite sides of the world, so our clocks are eleven hours apart. I called him early in his morning, but it is getting late into my night, so a few minutes later I tell him I'd better go. And he says:

DAD: OK. Thanks for calling. Happy Mothers' Day.

SON: Yeah, Happy Mothers' Day.

DAD: Umm...Daniel? Maybe I never will be—and I hope you can accept that—but if she were alive, I think she'd have been proud of you. For going. Even if she didn't understand. Even if she didn't agree with what you're doing. I think she would have been proud of you just for doing it. That's the kind of person she was. (Long, long pause.) All right. I'd better let you get to sleep. I do read your letters. Sorry I'm not very good at responding to them.

SON: It's OK.

DAD: K. Take care. I'll talk to you in another seven months. Bye.

SON: Bye. (To audience.) On P-day, I find myself wanting to tell Christy what happened. I don't know how, though, so I take my pen and paper, and I tell her instead all about the mangosteen, the queen of fruits, with its thick bitter purple skin which you peel back for a tender white fruit that tastes like it comes straight out of Lehi's dream. (More directly to audience.) I wish I could give you one, let you live a few moments in the sheer sensation of it, but they don't ship well. The only way to find out what it's like is to go there, preferably in May when Thai towns have their fruit festivals. Find a tree to take it straight off.

And you will know the moments of paradise that lie on the path of the hardest journeys.

(Black.)

CHRISTY: Scene nine. Here.

(Lights up.)

CHRISTY (cont.): Dear Daniel—I mean "Elder Pratt"—, At the time

I am writing this, you'll be home in twenty days, and yes, I've been counting. I know you didn't want me to do anything like that, but I figured as long as I didn't write anything distracting for you, I'd let myself count. Work hard, be good, do what's right… (Beat.) I just transferred to OSU, so I'll see you when you get back. —Christy. P.S. Your dad says hi.

SON: Christy, depending on how fast the mail goes, I might be back before this letter.

I was pretty good at not missing you too much all through my mission…but I'm starting to, now. I want you to know that you shouldn't have transferred, but since you did, I plan to take advantage of that. See you soon. And since you're apparently hanging out with my dad, tell him hi for me.

(Dark. Sounds of a plane landing.)

(Lights up. SON walks into the light where father is waiting.)

DAD: Hey.

SON: Hey. (Pause.)

DAD: How are you?

SON: Good.

(DAD looks him over. Puzzled.)

DAD: I think you've grown.

(Lights shift.)

SON: Some missionaries come back to banners, big signs, balloons maybe? I don't know; I've never actually seen it. I imagine it could be that way, though.

My dad is in an old plaid shirt and jeans. His expression is steady and neutral, though his face is ever so slightly more worn than before. As we drive home, he asks me about Thailand, and we talk for a while about plants and rocks. He seems pleased at how many details I noticed and remembered. I don't talk about the mission part yet because I'm still not ready to feel out how much he wants to know.

When we get home, dinner is leftover Spanish rice and microwave burritos. There's no need to slaughter a fatted calf because he knows I'm never really coming home in the fullest sense, never returning to the way he raised me. But the day-old rice is comforting and familiar, and the microwave burritos are nostalgically warm.

He passes me a second helping of sour cream and salsa, and it's quiet for a few moments.

I am content just to sit here, and remember the feeling of this house, content to know that he will always be my father, and that for this life, at least, I am his Prodigal Son.

Who Do You Think You Are?

ANGELA HALLSTROM

FROM *Bound on Earth*

THE TARDY BELL rang five minutes ago, and Mr. Glassing still hasn't shown up. Every day for the last six months, I've known exactly where to find him: standing in front of the chalkboard marking off our names on the roll, handing out his "how ya doin's" and "good to see ya's." He likes to watch us all come in so we don't get out of control before class starts, and it works. There's never much messing around here in seventh period Honors English 9. And now he's gone five minutes and everybody's acting crazy, sitting on top of their desks and shouting across the room. It's a zoo. Mr. Glassing would be so disappointed.

"He's bailed for sure," my good friend Rhonda says, and she looks all happy about it. Pleased as punch, as my mom would say. I want to strangle her. "I bet we could just leave and we wouldn't even get in trouble."

I don't respond. I keep my eyes on the door, my ears tuned in to catch the sound of his footsteps in the hall.

"Hello in there?" Rhonda says. I turn and look at her, trying to keep my face expressionless. She sighs and stalks away from me, over to a group of girls sitting on an empty book cart. But I don't care. It's better, anyway, that she doesn't know. If she did, she would either faint or die laughing, and today's been such a hard day already that I don't think I could handle either. So let her think I'm a goody-goody. A kid obsessed with following the rules. Because how could I tell her? A *teacher*? Mr. Glassing? Rhonda even makes fun of him, hooking her thumb through her belt loop like he sometimes does and strolling around, waving her free hand in the air and saying, "Iambic pen*tameter*. The rhythm of the *Gods*," which most kids think is hilarious. I never laugh, but it doesn't seem to stop her. She can be oblivious when she wants to be.

But it's good she doesn't know my secret. Nobody does, not even him. Sometimes I feel like a blinking neon sign whenever he comes within five feet of me, but so far, most people seem to think I like him in the way a kid's supposed to like a teacher. I respect him; I look up to him; I want to make him proud of me. Nobody's asked me, "Hey, Beth. Do you love him?" And if they did, I don't think I could deny it. I would have to say, Yes, I admit it. You've got me. I'm in love with my teacher, nine years older than me. It would be shocking, I know, and inappropriate and wrong. But I also think it might feel good to say it out loud: I love Brian Glassing. I love Brian Glassing. Terrible and wonderful and true.

I MET Mr. Glassing six months ago, the first day of my ninth grade year. I walked into class and saw him standing in front of the chalkboard, his legs straddled wide like a guitarist in a band, his hands stuffed all casual in his pockets. He had a shaggy goatee, not clipped and groomed like most guy teachers', and he wore a T-shirt with a picture of Shakespeare on it underneath his blazer.

"People!" he said, and Rhonda rolled her eyes. She absolutely hates it when teachers call us "people." She says it's rude.

"First thing, no screwing around. Understand? This is serious business in here. Words are serious. Poetry is serious. These guys and these ladies," he said, sweeping his arm in an arc along the *Authors of the World* display hanging around the room, "they are serious. You will not disrespect them, nor me, nor each other. You good?"

A couple of spiky-haired boys sitting next to me laughed into their hands. Mr. Glassing didn't seem to notice.

"So. Seating chart."

Everybody groaned.

"Where's the trust?" Rhonda asked, but Mr. Glassing acted like he didn't hear her.

"Today," he said, "the alphabet starts with the letter P. For Positivity. For Perseverance. And for a Passion for Poetry and Prose. All qualities that I hope you will diligently strive to obtain."

He paused, smiling. He seemed to be half joking. Making fun of himself. Some of the kids in class weren't buying it but everyone was listening.

"Just because you've always done a thing one way doesn't mean that you can't mix it up. Change it. Bend the rules. Like the alphabet. Who says we always have to start with *A*?"

We all looked at each other, a little confused. Were we supposed to answer this question?

"I mean, who says?" He moved his gaze around the perimeter of the room where we all stood with our books clutched against our chests, none of us saying a word. "Okay, then," he said. "Palmer, Elizabeth." He slapped his hand on the desk right across from his.

The name, of course, was mine. I slid into my seat, and he looked at me straight on for a couple seconds. His eyes were green and alive.

"El numero uno," he said. The number one. For the first time in my memory, my name was called first at school.

SO ALL MY PROBLEMS started this morning, when Mr. Glassing decided to show a movie called *Ordinary People* in his honors classes without sending home parental permission slips. Here in Utah, rated-R movies are huge no-no's. Even a lot of parents don't watch them, and those who do usually feel a little guilty about it, since everybody knows it's more or less against Church rules. It's not a *commandment* really, like "Thou shalt not steal," or "Thou shalt not commit adultery." It's more like a really powerful suggestion, such as not mowing your lawn in your bikini, which a neighbor of mine, Mrs. Probert, did for about three weeks one summer until she started getting notes of complaint left in her mailbox.

Mr. Glassing first tried showing the movie in second period. Unfortunately for him, Katie Carmichael and Julia DeOlivero—tattletales, both of them—are in that class. Jordan Fronk's in second period too—a kid who recently tried to start a petition to ban Coke from school premises because it contains caffeine and is therefore against the Word of Wisdom. Apparently the three of them met in a huddle after class, marched to the principal's office in a self-righteous huff, and blew the story open.

By lunchtime, the whole honors crowd knew what had gone down. All the kids at my table were buzzing, but I could barely swallow my peanut butter sandwich. We found out that the principal, Mr. Dunning, had called Mr. Glassing to his office right in the middle of third period and let him have it. Katie and Julia retold the story to anybody who would listen.

"Molly Mormon butt-kissers," Rhonda said. Rhonda is Catholic and has very little patience with the rest of us. "Did you know that Jordan Fronk says his mom is coming later today? I guess she's getting together with some other moms and they're bringing a list."

"What?" I said. "A list of all the ways that Mr. Glassing has taught us and sacrificed for us and basically made English fun instead of boring and painful?"

"You wish," Rhonda said. "I'm sure it's your basic Mormon

Lady list: this book had swearing, that story had a pregnant teenager, and stop setting a bad example by not wearing socks with your shoes."

I suggested that we start our own petition in support of Mr. Glassing, but none of the other kids at the table seemed too excited about it. Most of them, in fact, were just ticked at being cheated out of the chance to watch a video in class which, rated-R or not, is a luxury never to be messed with.

But I was nervous. What if Mr. Glassing got in real trouble? What if he got so mad that he decided to heck with all of us? It was embarrassing, sometimes, being these sheltered Mormon kids who never got to experience Real Life or understand True Art. I could tell Mr. Glassing felt sorry for us. He grew up in Chicago and had backpacked in Europe and visited Japan and settled here, he said, because he liked to mountain bike and ski.

"I had no idea," he would often say in class, and then go on to tell a story about liquor laws or stores closed on Sunday or Republican city councils. Most kids in class liked these stories and encouraged them, not because they particularly enjoyed our state being mocked, but because any time you can get a teacher on a topic that doesn't relate to actual learning it's a bonus.

But the stories worried me. I wanted him to like Utah, to like Mormons. To like me. To never leave.

I knew that during fourth period, Mr. Glassing had the Regulars—not the honors kids, not even the college-prep kids, but the lowest on the totem pole before you hit remedial—and that he had second lunch, so he'd still be in the classroom. The conversation at the lunch table had turned. Mr. Glassing's little scandal had been forgotten already and dismissed like yesterday's news, but I couldn't get him out of my head. I had to go to him and make sure he was okay. I stood up from the table.

"Hey, Beth! Where you going?" Rhonda yelled.

"Nowhere!" I said, tossing my lunch in the trash. "I mean, I forgot something. I need to do something."

Class time was almost over, and I had only a few minutes to

get to his room on the other side of the building. I knew if I could see him, watch him teaching for just a minute, I would know if he was okay. I can tell his moods really easily now—just one look, one certain gesture, like how he clenches and unclenches his hands when we're getting on his nerves. Before I got to his room, I could hear his voice filling up the hall.

"Your time is up," he was saying. I was so relieved to hear it, I didn't care how tense he sounded.

I peeked around his door and saw him whipping up and down the aisles, snatching worksheets from students' desks. Grammar worksheets, I could see. The kids in the room were all quiet and looked just a little bit afraid—quite a feat, considering they're the Regulars—and I knew right away that Mr. Glassing was mad. Grammar worksheets were a dead giveaway. He hates them and tells us so and, so far, has only threatened to use them as a punishment. I watched as he stalked around the classroom, tight-lipped, silent, daring the kids to make a sound. He was punishing them—and through them, all of us—for our narrow-mindedness, our clenched-up sensibilities.

When the bell rang, he didn't even say good-bye to his class. He just sat at his desk scowling down at the papers in front of him, passionately circling all the errors with a felt-tipped red pen. I stood there, shifting in my shoes, while his students pushed past me. But then I thought, "Do it, Beth. If you're going to do it, do it."

"Mr. Glassing?" I said.

He looked up, seemingly surprised to see me in the doorway.

"I just wanted to tell you we're not all like that. Like Katie and Julia and Jordan. Some of us appreciate art. Some of us don't tell on people."

He tilted his head at me in a tender kind of way. He breathed in through his nose and let a slow sigh out his chest. Then he smiled.

"You're one of the good ones, Beth. It's kids like you. This is why I do it, you know? For kids like you."

His eyes were soft and heavy and sad, and I wanted to go to him, to hold out my arms and watch him fold into them. I wanted to say, "I understand, I understand," smooth his hair, feel his heart beating. Instead I stood for a few hot seconds in the silence, looking into his face until I couldn't stand it anymore and had to look down.

"I'll see you seventh period," I said.

"See you then."

And he bent back over his desk, his red pen suspended, busy with correction.

THIS IS WHY I love Mr. Glassing:

He's kind. He gives students his home phone number to call if they have questions or problems or just want to talk. I've called twice with supposed homework questions, and he was very pleasant and patient on the phone both times. He has two cats named Elinore and Baby, and he lets both of them sleep in his bed. He helped build a house for Habitat for Humanity last summer.

He's smart. He double-majored in English and philosophy in college and once won an essay contest about Thoreau. (Or Emerson. I keep getting them confused. The one who went off into the woods.) He uses words like "parsimonious" and "fruition" and makes it seem natural.

He's handsome, but not in an obvious kind of way. His nose is a little on the big side, but I'm okay with it because it makes him look regal and unique. He has long, sensitive fingers, like you'd find on a painter or a pianist. His eyes literally change color: green some days, then gray, sometimes a mossy hazel. He smiles with his whole face.

He listens to the same kind of music I listen to, older bands like Depeche Mode and The Cure. During our poetry unit. he let us bring songs we liked, lyrically, and he played them during journal free-writing time. He picked some of his favorite songs and typed the words up for a handout so we could understand that poetry isn't just written by boring dead white guys.

He told me that I'm bright. In front of the whole class. He'd asked a question about *The Lord of the Flies*, something about symbolism and the pig's head on a stick and the nature of evil, and when none of us raised our hands he looked right at me and said, "Beth, you're so bright, you should have no trouble figuring this one out." When I answered, it I must have impressed him because he said, "See? There you go."

Sometimes, when he comes up behind me to check my work, he puts his hands on my shoulders. He hardly ever does this to anyone else.

SO ALL THAT HISTORY brings me to this moment: sitting here in seventh period, waiting for him to show, fear and anticipation wrestling around in my stomach. When I finally hear footsteps coming down the hall, they're flat and heavy and slow. It's easy to tell they're not Mr. Glassing's. I recognize the guy who comes into the room, but I don't know his name. He's big and redheaded, sweaty on his forehead, a shop guy or a coach.

"Settle!" he shouts.

A kid on the front row asks, "Where's Mr. Glassing?"

Mr. Shop Guy glares at him. "The million-dollar question. All I know is it's my prep period, and the last thing I want to do is hang out up here babysitting all of you because your teacher had a temper tantrum."

There's a bit of spit collected in the corners of his mouth. His teeth are gray.

"This is English class, right? So read a book. Write a poem. Diagram a sentence. Whatever it is you do in here—do it quiet. All right?"

It doesn't take much, usually, to scare an honors crowd into silence. Everybody reaches into his backpack to pull out paper and pencils and books. Except me. I refuse to move. The substitute sinks down into Mr. Glassing's chair with a grunt. He's four feet away from me, and I think I can smell his breath.

"Hey," he says to me. "If you're just going to sit there gazing off, at least put a book in front of your face and pretend to do something."

I look him right in the eye. I'm not afraid of this tough guy, this imposter. I don't want him to be here any more than he does.

"So you got something to do?" he asks.

I don't even hesitate. I don't even think.

"As a matter of fact, I do." Then I stand up, turn my back on him, and make my way to the door.

"Beth," I hear Rhonda hissing. "What are you doing?"

I don't turn around and answer. I just go.

I'M A PRETTY GOOD KID. I'm the youngest in a family of three girls and my nickname at home is "Lo-Main," short for low maintenance. My mom and dad and me, we actually like each other, which is pretty rare, I know. My dad has always been a softy, and my mom's undergone some kind of metamorphosis—maybe it has to do with menopause—and has given up on being strict now that I'm the only one left at home. Not that they let me do whatever I want or anything. I have curfews, some chores. But I think my mom is over being ultra-vigilant by now. She basically breathed right down my other sisters' necks most of their adolescence and got, as she likes to say, mixed results. So I don't think she has any energy left to be suspicious. And I don't give her many reasons to worry. I play clarinet in the school band; I get good grades; she knows most of my friends and my friends' families. I've never had a boyfriend. She comes to my room sometimes at night and flops on my bed and wants to talk about friends and feelings and if there's anything I need to get off my chest, and then I usually tell her a thing or two so she feels like she's doing her job. Then she leaves me alone until the mood strikes her again. It's our system. It works pretty well for both of us.

But I wonder what she'll say to me tonight. I'm sure they're going to call her. I've never been suspended—I've never even had a teacher call with anything but good news—but I can imagine how the conversation might go.

"Mrs. Palmer?" they'll say. "Your daughter Beth walked right out of Honors English 9, and nobody has seen her since. We think she left the building."

And then my mom will faint.

Although I haven't left the building, not yet. Right now I'm sitting on the toilet in the girls' bathroom so I can contemplate my next move. I can't go back to class—that much is certain. What I need is information. What happened to Mr. Glassing? Where has he gone?

And then, like a miracle, my answer appears. Jordan's mom, Mrs. Fronk, comes swinging into the bathroom with her little gang of ladies. I can see them through the crack in the bathroom door, and they all look flushed and beaming and thrilled. I tuck my feet up so they can't see me.

"I say, 'Good Riddance,'" says a freckly blonde.

"It's about time," another woman answers. She opens the door to the stall next to mine.

"Who will protect the children if not the parents? The government? Never. Hide their heads in the sand—that's what they do. The unions pay them to do it," says Freckly.

"It's enough to make a person want to homeschool," Mrs. Fronk says.

I sit on my toilet seat and listen to them. With each passing moment, I get more and more concerned. Good riddance? What, exactly, does this mean?

"That teacher never said a word," Mrs. Fronk says. "Not one word in his own defense. Now, that's the behavior of a person with a guilty conscience, if you ask me."

"I don't know," says the voice in the stall next to mine. "He didn't look too guilty to me."

"More like mad," says Freckly.

"Did you see the way he looked at Mr. Dunning? If looks could kill, I tell you what."

"Well, whether or not he knows that he's guilty isn't the

point," says Mrs. Fronk, rubbing her hands under the drying machine. "The point is, he's gone. And we didn't even have to get him fired. He left of his own free will and accord, and that's just great by me."

I think I'm going to be sick. If they could only see themselves like I see them: ridiculous in their Wal-Mart clothes, their ten-dollar haircuts. They think they have some kind of right to march into my life and kink it all out of joint? They think they're righteous or something? I see their faces. I can see the thrill in their eyes, the joy they took in making him squirm. Just who do they think they are?

Then I remember what Mr. Glassing always told us: Be passionate. Be daring. Go with your gut. So I will. I will. I know what I've got to do.

I KNOW WHERE Mr. Glassing lives. It's a little blue house with dingy shutters and a falling-down carport in North Salt Lake. I've been here three times. It's creepy, I know, like I'm a stalker or something. And I've even done stalkerish things, like sitting on a bench at the park across the street pretending to read a magazine while I wait for his car to pull in the driveway, or opening his mailbox to see what's inside it. Once, when nobody was home, I even dared to go right to the front door and peek through the living room window, and I saw his couch and the outline of his dining room table. All three times I came here, I just told my mom I was going to Rhonda's, but then I walked out the door, caught a bus, and rode my way to his house. The first time was the scariest—two connections and I got a little lost in his neighborhood, which isn't the best part of town—but each time I did it, I felt better. I crept along these unfamiliar sidewalks with my hair hanging down over my face, shielding my eyes, and it was like I was invisible but powerful, a featureless, nameless girl who was liable to do anything. Anything!

He's never seen me here. But today is the day. How alone he

must feel, abandoned, betrayed. And angry, of course, angry, and I need to talk him out of any rash decisions. I can convince him; I'm sure of it. If only he'll listen to me, he will understand how important he is to me and to all of us, how without him, nothing will ever be the same.

I sit on the park bench across the street from his house, and I can see his Chevy parked in the carport. Some little Hispanic kids are playing inside the plastic tunnels and slides at the park behind me, shrieking and yelling, ignoring their mother who wants them to come down. She's threatening them in Spanish, counting to three. "Uno! Dos! Tres!" she keeps yelling. They aren't listening to her. I decide she's counting for me. Spurring me on. The next countdown's mine.

"Uno!" she cries. Her face is red, insistent.

"Dos!" The children are laughing at her, hiding somewhere up in the tunnel beyond her reach.

"Tres!" I stand up.

A car splashes along the rain-wet road, and I wait for it. I keep my eyes on Mr. Glassing's door as it passes. Then I walk, my heartbeat steady and loud, my feet keeping even time like a marching soldier. I don't give myself a minute to stop or think or question. I raise up my hand, and I knock.

Silence. Quiet. I peer inside the window. The house is dark and motionless. Behind me, the Hispanic women and her children trudge down the sidewalk, away from the park and from me. I'm alone on the street. Even the wind has stopped blowing, and the world is still: the trees, the air, the clouds in the sky. I feel like I'm a girl in a movie and people are watching me, hushed and expectant.

I ring the doorbell and hear the chime echoing inside his walls. Just when I think no one is coming, I hear the thump of footsteps. My heart picks up speed.

The door opens. A strange, skinny guy in a tank top peers around the door at me, suspicious. His hair is curly and wild, and I wonder if I just woke him up.

"Yeah?" he says.

I start to say excuse me, wrong house, somehow, wrong guy, but then I remember. Donnie! It's Donnie! The new guy, the roommate who just came to live with him, an old friend from college who's trying to break into the world of professional snowboarding. He works as a bartender. Sleeps all day. Of course!

"Donnie?" I say. My voice sounds very small. I keep my hands tucked behind my back so he won't see them shaking. "Is that right?"

"Yeah," he says again, but slower this time.

"Is Mr. Glassing here?" I say. "I mean, Brian? Is he home?"

Donnie leans out the door and looks up and down the street. "How did you get here?"

"A bus. Well, a couple of buses," I say. He continues to look at me expectantly. "I took a transfer?" I explain, and laugh nervously.

"And how old are you?"

I realize there's no point in lying. He's onto me already.

"Fourteen."

"Hmm," he grunts. "You from school?"

I nod.

"So you know that Brian's pissed?"

So Mr. Glassing is home. He's already told Donnie the whole story. "Yes," I say. "I just wanted to talk to him. Tell him we're all really sorry. Tell him he needs to come back to school tomorrow."

"Well, good luck with that!" Donnie laughs. He leans against the doorframe, filling up the space.

"So can I talk to him?"

"Oh. Sorry. He's not here. Took off for a minute. He'll be back, though. Pretty soon. You want to wait?" He gestures inside the house.

I pause. I think, *Strange man, empty house, no witnesses, missing girl.*

"I'm just heading out. Leaving right now," he says. He jangles a set of keys in his hand. "But you're welcome to wait."

I wonder where this Donnie is heading, looking like he just rolled out of bed. "You're sure?"

"No problem. Just chill. He'll be back any minute." Then he swings his arm out and lets me inside Mr. Glassing's house. Without even giving me a backward glance, he skips down the front stairs, twirling his keys on his finger. Before I know it, he's gone.

And now I'm alone in Mr. Glassing's house. I sit very quietly on his saggy plaid couch. I've always known Mr. Glassing isn't a materialistic person, but looking around this place, I'm even more sure of it. There's nothing in his living room but this ancient sofa, a couple of beanbag chairs, and a boxy old television with rabbit ears. No plants. No stereo system. I crane my neck so I can see into his kitchen, and at least he's hung a poster in there: a print of that famous screaming guy, with the melty face and bugged-out eyes. I wish I could remember who painted it, or what it's called. Talking about the poster could be an icebreaker. A point of discussion.

I sit patiently for what seems like a long time, running possible conversation starters through my mind. *Guess who? Just thought I'd stop by! I bet you never thought you'd see me here!* At least a half hour goes by before I realize I've got to go to the bathroom, but I'm a little afraid to stand up. I know it's irrational, but I feel like I might trip some alarm, or Mr. Glassing might walk in at that exact moment and think I'm in here to ransack his place. But when you've got to go, you've got to go. I stand. Nothing happens.

I creep to the bathroom and push the door open. A film of soap and dust coats the counter. The shower curtain is swept back, and I notice the floor of the tub is gray and unscrubbed. I'm sure if I leaned over I could carve my initials in it with my fingernail. I don't let myself think about the toilet and how long it has gone without a good cleaning.

When I stand at the sink to wash my hands, I look at the items Mr. Glassing has lined up along the counter—shaving cream, a plugged up razor, deodorant, a comb—and before I know what's gotten into me, I pick up each one and turn it over in my hands. I squirt a pillow of shaving cream into my palm and rub it between my fingers, and when I bring my hands up to my nose, I smell spicy and sharp, like a man.

I look at my face in the mirror and pretend he's waiting just outside the door for me. I pull his comb through my own dark hair and study my face from different angles. My cheeks are too round, and my lips are too narrow, but if I tilt my chin a certain way and push my mouth out, I look better. Suddenly his cats, Baby and Elinore, appear. They slide up against my shins purring. I reach down to pet them.

"Hello, kitties," I whisper. "Hello, girls."

They saunter out of the bathroom and down the hall, and I follow them into what must be Mr. Glassing's bedroom. His clothes lie in little mounds all over the floor. I check out the window. No one is coming. I stand very still and listen, and I can't hear a thing. I am alone here, I tell myself. No one will know.

I lie down on his unmade bed. His pillowcase needs washing, but I bury my face in it just the same and the scent of him—new paper, wet ground—rises up and into me.

I close my eyes, and then I hear it. A car, slowing and turning. I scramble out of bed and see a blue Volkswagen pulling into the driveway. Mr. Glassing is inside it; and driving, a woman with curly blonde hair.

I'VE BEEN SITTING in Mr. Glassing's closet for close to fifteen minutes, too scared to listen to them very well. My heart is pounding in my ears, my hands are shaking, and I'm thinking, *What will I do or say if they find me?* A fourteen-year-old girl, crazy and pathetic, crammed in among my English teacher's loafers and tennis shoes for no explainable reason. But it seems as if they're not coming in here after all. At least not yet. And I know that I've got to get out of here before they do, because even if they don't open the closet, I couldn't bear listening to what might go on.

I open the closet door and start to stand. Then I hear him say, "These kids," and I can tell he's angry. He's talking to this woman—I have heard her name, it's Marianne—about us. About me.

"These kids," he says, "they're like little robots. No thinking for themselves! No self-expression. I can't stand it."

"But if you just stick it out three more months, Brian. Think about it. Do you really want this on your record? Quitting and everything? You know you want to teach college, and if you just up and quit, it'll look bad."

"But I'm climbing the walls in there, Marianne. These kids look up at me with their big, dumb, glazed-over expressions, and I think, 'Dupes! All of you!' It's sad, is what it is. I feel like, anymore, teaching them is just a waste of time."

"It's not a waste."

"It is! It is! They think they've got everything figured out, you know. They look at me with those sour little judgmental eyes."

"Every last one of them?"

"Every last one."

"Come on."

"I mean it. If there was one kid—even one—that I thought was worth fighting for, I'd stay. But you know what? To hell with them. To hell with all of them."

I can't believe it's Mr. Glassing—*my* Mr. Glassing—in there talking. I want to pound my fist against his bedroom wall. I want to yell, *Shut up!* to make him stop, to make him realize that he's ruining everything. Who is this girl? Why are you trying to impress her? Why are you lying to her, telling her things you don't really believe, acting nothing like the man I know you are: kind, good, patient, open-hearted? You looked at me, Mr. Glassing, and you told me things with your eyes. Don't deny it! That you were proud of me, that I was smart, that you were glad to see me every day and teach me and that you saw great things in my future. "Teaching is the greatest job on earth," you told us, and we believed you. "Call me," you said. "Any time. I care about you guys." And you did, you do, I swear it.

"Mormons are impossible," Marianne says. "You know this. There's no changing them."

"Free me from their clutches!" he says, and she giggles, high and breathy, like a cheerleader.

I realize now I've got to leave. I'm afraid I'm going to cry and he will hear me. I sneak out into the hall.

"But you don't want to let them ruin your career," she says. I see them together on the couch, his arm slung around her shoulder like he owns her, her body curled into his. "All they want from you is a little apology, a little yessir, nossir, you're right, I'm wrong. You can suck it up and go back there in the morning. Torture those kids with worksheets and spelling tests. It'll bore them to tears and keep you safe. Then you can come back home to me every night, and I'll make things all good again."

"Promise?" he says.

"Don't I always make things better?"

She turns toward him and tilts her head up and they kiss. I hear their wet lips parting. The bathroom door stands open, and I see my own reflection in the mirror: small, pale, a sliver of a person. I may as well be a ghost. Who did I think I was, coming here? Trying to claim this man, or save him? He knows nothing about me. I'm here in his house, and he can't even tell.

They've stopped talking. I know what they're doing. I stand behind them silent as night. Their heads have disappeared from above the couch, but I can see their legs, intertwined, hanging off the edge. I wonder how long I can stand here staring, breathing, until the sheer force of my presence forces them up and around to look right into my face. I hear his name in my mind: Brian Glassing. Brian Glassing. Loud enough it almost seems outside me. Its rhythm fits the rhythm of my raging heart.

They don't notice me. I walk by them without a sound. I go to his front door and pass through, leaving it open behind me, letting the screen door slam, because if he hears it and comes looking, it won't matter. He won't recognize me. I'll just be a kid on the street with my back to him, walking away from him, some girl he never knew.

A Feeling in Your Head

LANCE LARSEN

FROM *Iowa Review*

TO HER CREDIT, and perhaps to my own arrested artistic development, my mother saved none of my creations from childhood. She kept no box packed with all things Lance: no pipe cleaner animals, no doily Valentines or pudgy hand impressions in plaster, no compositions titled My Favorite Animal or If I Were President, no stupid limericks copied from the board about the boy who said ain't and fell in a can of red paint. In fact, the only evidence that any higher learning took place my first two years at Washington Elementary fell into my lap—or more precisely, into my cereal bowl—during Christmas break, thirteen years later, when I was home for college. There, where I intended to pour my cornflakes, I found "Hope"—a child's composition my father had unearthed the night before cleaning out his office. I took it in: misspelled words, labored printing, words bunched together like cars after a train wreck. The paper had a pulpy tooth to it, with a faint dotted line to keep baby letters in their place but allow a few privileged tall guys (d f h k l t) to stand straight and flex their muscles. Here is the composition, in its entirety:

> I hope that the war going on in veiknomb will stop
> real soon. I hope that my uncle won't get hurt
> in veiknomb. thoses are two seteces yousing hope.
> Hope is a word something like the word wish.
> hope is a word that you can not draw like you can
> draw a tree. It is a feeling in your head.

And there, in the upper right hand corner, my name. Back then, I hadn't yet learned from recess taunts that Lance rhymed with "dance," "romance," and "pee your pants" or that Larsen was as common as chewed gum—check any phone book. Back then, the alliteration of the capital l's made for a delicious mouthful. Back then, Lance Larsen sounded regal, not as it does now, like the name of a minor character in a Hollywood soap, someone that betrays his best friend then dies in a car wreck, but has great hair till the end.

But when did I write this essay? If it was first grade, picture tiny, bird-like, wizened Mrs. Pew (pee-You, we pronounced it behind her back, holding our noses, as if something smelly had escaped into the room), and behind her, a bank of windows facing my house. If in second grade, think of sleeveless, buxom, unmarried Miss Welch, whom I associated with delicious grape juice, windows looking west toward the train yard. But in both cases, trees. My school had plenty of those. Giant oaks circled the playground, branches tossing—a kind of hope.

Hope was everywhere, in fact. Hope walked me to school, hid inside the spiked pods of fallen chestnuts, bubbled up cold from the drinking fountain, rose with us when we covered our hearts and made promises to a limp flag, circled the room like an agitated hummingbird above our motley voices. Saying names of classmates out loud, this too was hope. George Gregorias: from Greece, who spoke not a word of English, and was so out of touch with Idaho that he wore sandals and shorts to school. Donna Gibbs: from an even bigger and more friendly country called Texas, where people rode horses and drilled for oil and spoke as if they were in old timey movies: "Hi ya'll," Donna said, "my family and me—we just moved here." Grant Somebody: who gobbled paste and couldn't follow the simplest instructions, like how to cut a round pumpkin from square paper, but more than once pulled out his wankeroo in class and dribbled urine to show girls how boy plumbing worked, then scuffed away the evidence with his shoe. Most remarkable, though less notorious, was Todd Hunter—who drew soldiers just before a bullet sent them to their great reward.

But the hope I mentioned in my essay—"I hope that the war going on in veiknomb will stop real soon. I hope that my uncle won't get hurt in veiknomb."—was different. You had to ask for it in dinner prayers. I mean kneel-down-together-as-a-family-while-the-food-gets-cold prayers. Not to be confused with quickie blessings over breakfast and lunch. Dinner prayers took forever, and there was always the chance someone would walk past our kitchen window and see us on our knees getting religious.

I hated that, and adopted two strategies to cope. First, I kept one eye open, just in case someone came to the door. That way I could jump up and pretend I was retrieving a fallen fork. Second, to distract myself, I dropped tiny spit bombs to the carpet below. Entertainment, Idaho style. When I closed one eye and opened the other, the drip switched positions. Blink quickly, and the elongated drop jumped back and forth. During my experiments in depth perception and the elasticity of saliva, I didn't listen so much as let the prayer wash over me: bless the sick and afflicted, bless the widows, bless the missionaries, bless Grandpa Mac and his arthritis, bless Uncle Jim and let no harm befall him in Vietnam ....

Befall, befall. In Vietnam, bullets could befall you, missiles, booby trap bombs, shrapnel, even knives. If my uncle didn't come home, my Aunt Karen, a no-nonsense woman with blonde beehive hair, would be left alone to ride herd on my three cousins. But prayer could cancel all that dangerous befalling. When we blessed the food, the words stayed in the room. When we prayed on our knees, the prayers curled upwards, like steam from a vent, like the soul leaving a wounded body.

This is how it went for months. Each evening we'd pray my uncle safe. Each morning I'd go to school and copy Todd Hunter's war drawings. He knew how to draw every kind of scene: cavalry, Civil War, WW I, WW II, even Vietnam. Whether his fighter men were on horses or in trenches or on the back of an Army Jeep firing a machine gun, which is how I pictured my uncle, Todd made the dying real. Bazookas, shock waves, explosions, puddles of blood, gashes, limbs blown off, fallen comrades, the right kind of helmets: these helped. But bullets were the key. First freeze them in air, then draw dotted lines to show trajectory—and the waiting victims.

I never drew my uncle.

Safer that way, safer not to put him and bullets on the same page.

Drawing was the opposite of hope. It was a lot like knowing the future but not being able to stop it. With drawing, you could see catastrophe before it happened: who would walk away missing an arm, who would never walk away.

On winter Sundays, we entered the church for sacrament and sermons in afternoon light, then exited in darkness, as if our praying brought on the gloom, our singing caused it to lick at the chapel windows, our amens led it to press down on the station wagon my father maneuvered through the streets like an elegant hearse. "Abide with me; 'tis eventide. The day is past and gone; The shadows of the evening fall; The night is coming on." I sang this hymn and then carried it in my blood, and by the time we reached our driveway, which was long before the car warmed up, I'd feel the need for home like a fever.

We didn't lock our front door in those days, so I'd bound out of the car, always in a race against something, always the first to enter the sputtering warmth of the front hall. One night I flipped on the hall light, then headed for my room.

But froze mid-stride.

There in the living room, obscured by shadows, in my father's chair, sat a figure. Hands on arm rests, feet casually crossed at the ankle. Was he sleeping? Was he dead? I could barely make him out. What did he want with us? Did he have a gun? Was I supposed to warn my mom first or bravely confront the stranger? What approach would always-cool, always-three-steps-ahead Mannix the private investigator take? Would this shadow intruder vanish when I flipped on the light, as they sometimes did in *The Twilight Zone*?

"Hey, there," the man said from the darkness.

I jumped back into the hall and bumped into my mother.

"A robber," I said. I hissed it.

"What are you talking about?"

"In there," I said, jerking my thumb toward the living room. "What do we do?"

Without hesitation, brave as Ginger the wonder girl spy of many disguises on *Mission: Impossible*, she flipped on the lights. In that silence, they looked each other over. If atoms ever reverberate between stares, they ricocheted off each other that evening, or rebounded, or did whatever atoms do under such circumstances. Then my mother smiled.

"Jim," she said, "you're back." And walked across the room.

He stood up then, my uncle, laughing a little and holding a bottle of homemade strawberry jam.

"It got cold outside in the truck," he said, "and I couldn't ignore the hospitality of an unlocked door."

They hugged each other, jam still in his hand, and my mother wouldn't let go of him. Then my dad and my two sisters and I got in on the act—as if trying to cancel the years he'd been deployed.

What had it been like in the jungle?

When I stepped away, I looked him over. No uniform, but his hair was still cut short. He'd been a star quarterback in high school, had pictures in the yearbook to prove it. He looked about the same, but a little older. No blown-off leg, no missing arm, no jagged scar running along his jaw. His forearms as tanned and muscled and hairy as ever. He had walked across the room without even a hint of a limp. And if there was shrapnel stuck forever in his body, he didn't show it.

"How about some waffles?" Mom said.

We entered the kitchen, all of us, and my mother got out the waffle iron, and whatever murkiness I had felt in the car leaked away in the bustle of our bright, warm kitchen. My parents and Uncle Jim talked the way adults do when they haven't seen each other, small talk, sentences started and abandoned, certain words rusty, questions zinging back and forth.

During supper, I looked Uncle Jim over again—his five o'clock shadow glowing dark, as if a second face lay hidden beneath this one. He looked at his plate the way you might read a map, then laid on a patina of butter, slicing with purpose, fork, knife, switching back and forth, as if his hands were detached from the rest of him. He swirled each piece of waffle in a smear of jam, chewed, then returned his fork for more—a prolific eater. I kept thinking of the other man, back in the living room, the man that occupied the room before my mother flipped on the light. Except for watching matinees at the Chief Theater, I almost never sat in the dark. How could he do it without getting scared? Like being wrapped in a cape when I got my hair cut, a cape that cut out the light. I could move my toes inside my shoes, flex my fingers, the usual things, but in the dark, everything turned secret. Was that hope? A feeling in your head. Not anything you could explain. Letting the dark wrap your face and the air settle on your skin. Cars driving by or silence, it didn't matter. And if you closed your eyes—did that change the feeling? It took guts and patience to sit there alone, to keep sitting. In someone else's house, in someone else's darkness, no special hurry to it, waiting for someone you love to turn on the lights.

A Sudden Pull Behind the Heart

PATRICK MADDEN

FROM *The Best Creative Nonfiction*, vol. 2

THIS ESSAY IS ABOUT three words I can barely make out in Latin on the cupola of the Catedral Metropolitana on the Plaza de Mayo in Buenos Aires. It's about a flailing attempt, in words, to recreate some bit of epiphany. It is about the fact that every Thursday afternoon, the grandmothers of disappeared children (they were mothers of the disappeared, too, once, but they have given up that hope) march in circles around the Plaza de Mayo, in front of the Catedral Metropolitana, in front of the Casa Rosada, the seat of government, from whose balconies Evita Peron once rallied the *descamisados*, the shirtless, before her death at age 33.

The grandmothers shuffle in their white shawls, in silent protest to the government that knows, to leaders and dealers left over from nearly a decade of "dirty war": military rule, midnight raids, tortures and assassinations, and the trade in infants across the borders with Uruguay and Chile.

Among so many who lost children and grandchildren: Juan Gelman, a poet, who was not home when they came for him, whose son and daughter-in-law were taken in his stead; Juan Gelman, whose son ended up in a barrel in the river Luján, a bullet in the back of his head; Juan Gelman, whose pregnant *nuera*, his daughter-in-law, was taken to the Hospital Militar in Montevideo, where she gave birth and then was murdered; Juan Gelman, whose new granddaughter was then given to a policeman whose wife was barren. So many pregnant women taken, raped, tortured, executed, their babies kidnapped. This story from Argentina. This story from Uruguay. This story from Chile. Military men who went to church on Sundays, to the machine on Mondays, to beat and prod and submerge and shock and threaten.

Juan Gelman, a poet, self-exiled to Mexico, whose granddaughter was eventually found by the Grandmothers of the Plaza de Mayo, those women whose work the six other days of the week when they are not marching in the square is re-membering, re-constituting families, pestering government officials, pressuring the press, searching in archives and unmarked graves, and they did find Macarena, as they had found over seventy children before her, and Juan Gelman was returned to his granddaughter in March of 2000. She was twenty-three years old, living in Montevideo, Uruguay. Her mother's body has not yet been found.

On a Monday in early April, the feast day of St. Ephiphanius, as my own country staged its invasion of Iraq, the grandmothers were not walking. As I walked about the Plaza de Mayo, I kept my eyes fixed, I sidestepped the dirty women languishing under the columns in front of the cathedral doors, I turned briskly to loose my garment from the grip of one who said "Please, anything you have, God bless you," I eluded another who moved into my path. I half-saw signs scrawled with statistics and sad stories. My downcast eyes scanned the frayed flannel edges of blankets, then returned to tracing the grout between the stones.

I entered the cathedral to escape the rabble. In my head swirled the story of this silver land on its silver river: this unbelievable, this brutal, methodical, mechanical, cold, unfeeling, this rage for order, this Process of National Reorganization, this maniacal torture of misidentity: children the age of my children kidnapped, scattered, unknowing. It was a story I barely knew, knew only in broken ideas and images, my own imagination's impositions on a history that had been hidden, ignored, nevertalkedof. I wondered if the disappeared children like Macarena Gelman might carry in their very DNA some inkling of who they were, if they might have natural genetic tendencies to seek justice for the downtrodden. I wondered of they naturally boiled over into heated arguments with their "parents" whose ideologies must have been at polar odds with their real parents, at least.

Inside the cathedral, it was almost silent. I saw the ornate arches, the wrought iron railings, the velvet chairs, the silver-plated altar, the faded frescoes, the gilded windowwork, the guarded tomb of José San Martin, liberator of Argentina, Chile, and Peru, born in rural Yapeyú, Argentina, of stately parents, educated in Europe, returned to set his people free. In a moment of calm, I cast my eyes upward forty meters to the cupola. There engraved, in Roman characters, I read three words: EGO VICI MUNDUM. It was all I could see within the rim.

Even before I could puzzle out its meaning, translate those words (think Freud, Caesar, French newspaper), I understood what it meant, and not only what it meant, but where it came from, who had said it, about what, and why. Jerome's Vulgate translation of John 16:33 reads, more completely: *In mundo pressuram habebitis: sed confidite, ego vici mundum*, which is to say "In the world ye shall have tribulation; but be of good cheer. I have overcome the world."

This was not the solution, a revelation for the revolution; this was not justice delayed and eternal rewards; it was no opiate. It was a sudden pull behind the heart, some opening to compassion, some inscrutable calm regardless, despite it all.

I left the cathedral then. Buoyed in spirit, introspective in mind, I walked out the cathedral doors, past the flyers in the foyers, beside the benedicted mendicants, among the twelve

Corinthian columns that grow from south to north as the earth drops away to the river-sea, close to the crest calling out SALVUM FAC POPULUM TUUM, into the good airs. I did not notice then the carved bas-relief watching over me in the pediment above, but I have since studied it, and I tell you that in that stone on the cathedral in Buenos Aires, there are sheep and cattle and calm camels in the corners above the cornices, in a reunion scene: ten repentant brothers and the brother they had disappeared, who was lost and then found, dead and then alive, sold by his siblings to be a slave and then turned their savior in time of famine. There is Jacob returned to his son Joseph: Israel's son is revealed, the ten are relieved, Benjamin is released. In this everlasting embrace, the father and the son keep watch over the plaza: the speeches and protests, marchers and merchants, the weekly silent procession of old women in kerchiefs keeping vigil, searching, remembering, so we may not forget.

Nothing in Particular

SCOTT RUSSELL MORRIS

FROM *Prick of the Spindle*

A witty remark proves nothing.
—VOLTAIRE

AS I HOPE you already inferred from the title, this essay is about nothing in particular. While discussing nothing, I want to talk about how sometimes when I am tired and I want to say something in class—something witty and educated, something that will show the teacher and the other students that I read all of the assignment, that I have applicable past experience, which I will so expertly bring into the class discussion—nothing comes out of my mouth, and instead I forget all the vocabulary of the English language, while words jumble around in my mind. I also want to talk about how I barely escaped Ashton, Idaho, a few weeks ago. I'm going to say a few things that I think I learned from my mom. I would like to say everything about how much I like squirrels, but I won't, because if I brought them up, they could take over the whole essay. Besides, they have nothing to do with this essay.

I should also admit that I realize *nothing* is a hopeless word. We all learned in first-grade writing, if not in preschool, that *thing* is not an acceptable word to use in a paper. It tells your readers nothing about what you are trying to say. Use something more specific, was always the teachers' advice. If you mean peach, say *peach*. If you mean the quadratic formula, say *quadratic formula*. The word *nothing* itself reminds me, every time I write it: "No thing! Don't use it!" And if *thing* is a no go, then *nothing* is a double negative, which I think is second-grade grammar.

A FEW WEEKENDS AGO, some friends (Tim, Andy, Jessie, and Jake) and I visited Tim's grandparents' farm in Ashton, Idaho. It had been snowing since we arrived late Friday night, but it was coming down particularly hard on Sunday. When we got out of church, there were another three or four inches of snow on the car, and the flakes were getting bigger. We drove back to the farm house slowly. There was almost no visibility; we might as well have been driving through a white void as we went out to the farm house. The picture is one I took from the side window. I hope you notice the disappearance of the sky and ground.

Nothing to see but flakes of snow. We arrived safely, though, since we discovered the road was marked on both sides by small posts which were not quite snowed over yet. Later that night, Tim's grandparents, and his aunt and uncle decided to go out again, and they got stuck on their way back.

"If we're not back by 6:30, call the sheriff," Tim's grandfather said, mostly in jest. At around 6:45, we got a call from a neighbor. Tim's grandparents had stopped by and, according to the neighbor, should have been home by now. We tried to call them on their cell phone. No answer. We were sure that they were fine. Around 7:30, when we were actually thinking about calling the sheriff, they finally called us. They got stuck in the snow not far away; could Tim drive the truck out to them? Tim, Jessie, and Andy, natives to cold weather and smart enough to bring snow clothes into the negative 20-degree weather and blizzard, put on their gear and charged into the night. I had nothing to offer, except that I lent Andy my gloves—the only warm items I'd brought—because in his haste, he couldn't find his. I watched as they got the truck, and then later when they resorted to the tractor with the snow blower attached. I watched from the farmhouse window, thinking how lame it was that I was doing nothing, that I could do nothing. I tried to justify that I was a Southern California boy, used to paradisiacal San Diego weather, not Idaho blizzards. But surely there was something I could do. It didn't help that earlier in the day, Tim's grandfather had said how all ten of their children were raised on the farm, and they knew how to work. My dad taught me to work, I was thinking. I helped him file, keep accounts, assemble mass mailings. And my mom, she had me vacuuming every Saturday before I could even think about cartoons.

Eventually I got up the courage and put on my one coat—a nice leather thing, perfect for those bone-chilling, 57-degree San Diego nights—and my tennis shoes. I went outside and started walking to where the snow blower was working. Andy came up the snow-covered driveway and told me to go back inside.

"There's nothing you can do," he said, handing back my gloves. "I was just standing there myself." So we both went inside, and when the whole family was back inside and warm, we had hot chocolate and wassail to celebrate the safe return.

THINKING MORE ABOUT the word itself, and how it is used, I think it is ironic that *nothing* should be a noun. A noun, the colloquial definition goes, is a person, place, or thing. Nothing certainly is not a person or a place. It is definitively not a thing, and yet this is how it is used grammatically. Really it's just an idea. Which means it doesn't exist, or rather exists only in our heads and on paper so that we have a notion of it. The early Babylonians did not have a notion of it. They had no way of using zero as we understand it. Instead they left a space where we would now put a zero, nothing to represent nothing. But that isn't good enough for modern thinkers. Maybe it is a sign of advanced thinking that nothing—absence—can so certainly be something—substance. There is nothing here, we say. Poets love such ambiguities. *Is* equals existence. *Nothing* equals zip, zilch, nil, null, zero, empty. And yet "There is nothing" still makes sense whether it is nothing to hear, see, do, read, watch, eat. We put something where nothing exists. I recognize that it is a good thing to differentiate between 1 or 10 or 100, especially on my paycheck, but outside of mathematics, why the obsession?

It may be because pure nothing does not exist, and recognizing that, we are forced to emphasize that something does exist where nothing is evident. The closest thing to *nothing* that I can think of is absolute zero, the point at which all energy is gone from a system and no matter is moving. But even this is just a theory and has never been seen. It may not exist, but it has been given a name anyhow, so that when it is discovered, it will already be known and placed neatly in our minds. Space closely approaches absolute zero at about 4°K, with the Boomerang Nebula being the coldest known place in the universe at a record 1°K. Almost nothing, but not quite—an honorable mention for the attempt though.

Vacuum also draws images of nothingness. The ideal vacuum means nothingness, but real world vacuums aren't nothing, they are just less. Significantly less pressure, less matter. Not no pressure or no matter. Space is also called a vacuum, suggesting that it is emptiness, but who can look at the stars and say that there is nothing in space? Is it because the stars are farther apart than we are used to? How close do objects have to be before the space between stops having nothing and suddenly contains both objects?

The truth is that there is *something* to eat, watch, read, do, see, hear; it just might not be what we want it to be. My mother taught me this lesson well enough:

"Mom, there's nothing to eat."

"Have an apple."

"There's nothing on TV."

"Read a book."

"I have nothing to write about."

I FEEL LIKE I should mention, before I ramble too far, that there is a difference between "nothing to do" and "boredom." I learned this lesson early. I am rather fond of having nothing to do. I think all too frequently people have far too much to do, and do they really get anything accomplished? I am not sure, maybe, but I like to think not, because their frantic nothing justifies my undisguised nothing. When I was a kid and would lie around the house in the most comfortable couch and the book I was reading, either finished or grown dull, would drop to the floor, I would just stare at the ceiling. My mom would then ask, "Are you bored? I can find something [meaning chores] for you to do."

"No." was always the response. Nothing trumps something every time. Society, however, does not share my personal opinion. For example, you run into an old friend you haven't seen in a while. After the normal pleasantries she asks:

"So what are you doing these days?"

"Nothing much," you reply. (Or at least, this is how I reply).

You (I) politely ask what she is doing.

"I am so busy…" and then she lists the societies she belongs to, the home and family improvement projects, the calendars she is juggling, her job, her classes, her dog, and onward. Who wins the conversation? All judges point to the busy one. While I politely give my condolences that she can't seem to find time for herself, it is understood that she is the superior being. Still, I always leave thinking I am in the better situation, the condolences polite and heartfelt. I like having time to do nothing.

Maybe the busy bee wins because everyone knows I lied. I say there is nothing, and yet there is something. Reading is something. Writing essays is certainly something. Reading a good book and then just staring at the ceiling while you think about it is something. I remember the first time that staring at the ceiling after reading a book wasn't just something, it was absolutely necessary. I was in eighth grade and I had just read *The Giver*. The ending baffled me; I was mad and delighted at the same time. I put the book down and stared at it first, and then at the ceiling and back at the book. It may have looked like I was doing nothing, but there was something going on inside me. The book was changing how I thought about good literature. Even though I was already someone who read all the time, this was my first glimpse at how good reading is for the soul, how moving and complicated books can be.

But still, we say there is nothing when really there is always something. Maybe it's something we don't want to repeat. Maybe it's something we don't care to mention because it is dull or uninteresting in present conversation with present company.

"What did you do at work today?"

"Nothing."

"What did you just say?"

"Nothing."

"What is your essay about?"

"Nothing."

(This page intentionally left blank.)

THE THEORY OF ABIOGENESIS, now commonly called *spontaneous generation*, was a common misconception that held sway from at least the time of Aristotle until the 1700s. Spontaneous generation holds that some complicated organic life forms are generated by the decomposition of other organic matter. Aristotle noted that aphids came from dew; maggots were generated by rotting meat; mice came from the old hay; and crocodiles were spawned by fallen logs in swamps. Essentially, it was a something-from-nothing approach to life.

When the first scientists began challenging these "vulgar errors," others lashed back. "To question [spontaneous generation] is to question reason," Alexander Ross wrote. The textbook experiment (and this was in my middle school, high school, and college biology books) shows a flask with meat in it. When the flask is left uncovered, maggots appear on the meat. When the flask is covered completely, nothing happens. When the flask is covered with a semi-permeable covering (meaning that air was still passing through it) maggots appeared on the covering, but not in the meat. Through these means, Francesco Redi determined that maggots did not come from rotting meat, but rather *omne vivum ex ovo*; "*Every living thing from an egg.*" Or, as Rodgers and Hammerstein lyricized:

> Nothing comes from nothing.
> Nothing ever could.

I LIKE THAT ZERO is the shape it is. 0. Just a line containing nothing, as though by encircling it in a line of something, anything, we might understand it. We know exactly what isn't there in the center. I also like that in tarot cards, the No. 0 card is the Fool and that the Fool is the one who experiences the brunt of the tarot story. The Fool is the cosmic adventurer, the perfect anthropomorphizing of existentialism, a symbol that the seeker needs to remove everything else from himself and start at the beginning again, to look at himself from his very core, with nothing else to distract him.

But I would hesitate to say that there is nothing at the core.

Common phraseology has it that, "In the beginning was the void," or "In the beginning there was nothing." But that isn't true. Genesis says, "In the beginning God created the heaven and the earth." There was God, and immediately a place for him to live and a place for us. Even secular science says there was something there; the Big Bang was an explosion of condensed matter. It may have been the only speck of matter in all of existence, but it was there tainting the nothingness of space with its inherent somethingness. Which was the superior, space or that condensed matter? Is it Nothing ruined by Something, or Something surrounded by Nothing? They Might Be Giants puts the question like this:

> Particle Man, Particle Man,
> ...Is he a dot, or is he a speck?
> When he's underwater, does he get wet?
> Or does the water get him instead?
> Nobody knows, Particle Man.

They also say that nobody knows the answer, so maybe I should give up now. But even if I can't answer the question, I still want to know which was more potent, the nothing or the something, and how the something had the audacity to BANG so that something permeates everything and nothing can be found nowhere.

I STILL HAVEN'T talked about wanting to say something when nothing is coming out. *On the tip of the tongue*, the expression goes, but *tumbling around in the mind* might be a better description. *Tumbling* isn't the right word either, because when rocks or jelly beans are put through tumblers, they come out polished. When my words flee and play hide-and-seek in my mind, I look foolish, not shiny. This morning I had the experience twice during the course of a single class. It was my research class. We were giving group presentations, spontaneously thrust upon us. I looked up the information in the textbook and took detailed notes, but when I got to the front of the class I couldn't remember what I was supposed to talk about. I looked at my notes; I had forgotten to write down the word I was supposed to be defining. I had all the specifications of what it entailed, what one should do to accomplish it successfully, but I had no word for the thing itself. I stammered. Nothing came to mind; I just stared at the spot on my notes where I should have written something. The word, my group mate whispered to me, was *method*. I was supposed to describe the word *method*.

Later in the class, I raised my hand to say something funny in response to what scientists do when their research doesn't go the way they want it to. The teacher called on me, and the words wouldn't come out. They lay flat in my mind, and the whole class was silent while I tried to speak. I had indicated I had something to say, and once that first something is articulated, something more is expected. To give nothing at that point is unacceptable. But there was truly nothing there, and the joke fell flat like week-old soda. Eventually I eked out that they put suggestions for further study in their Evaluation section. It didn't even come out funny.

I have nothing else to say. I hope you see the lie in that. I could go on for pages, really. On and on. I could talk about nothing *ad nauseum*, but I won't, because, while there might be something left to say, I'm done.

Solitaire

KATHRYN LYNARD SOPER

FROM *The Year My Son and I Were Born*

REED CRAWLED OFF the fold-out chair, stiff as a zombie. Neither of us had slept much. The prim nurse had appeared every hour to prod my womb with her blunt fingers, sending shooting stars of pain through my pelvis. Every time I jolted from sleep I remembered: Thomas.

The fuzzy numbness which had cocooned me the night before was gone, leaving me bare and blinking in the stark light of morning. Reed pulled on his sweatshirt, kissed me goodbye, and headed for the door. If he hurried, he could catch the next commuter train, then the bus that would take him home. Home, where our one car waited in the garage. in case my mother needed it. She'd flown to Utah from Maryland when my preterm labor started two weeks before, coming to my rescue just as she always did.

My earliest memory: I was two years old. My mother was

Excerpted from the book The Year My Son and I Were Born, *a mother's memoir of the emotional and spiritual transformation sparked by the birth of a disabled son. Kathryn Soper has been a speaker for the National Down Syndrome Congress. Copies of her book can be ordered at www.globepequot.com.*

holding me over the kitchen sink, my stomach pressed against the edge of the countertop, her arm wrapped around me from behind, her free hand scrabbling frantically at my face. Her long fingernails dug into my mouth, scratching the back of my tongue and the top of my throat. The white, knobby top of a chicken leg was wedged in my airway, just beyond her reach. I tasted fright on her knuckles and palm. In the emergency room, doctors opted to wait until my stomach emptied to remove the piece, to avoid the high risk of aspiration and possible death. My mother sat at my bedside for hours as I slept, her hand on my chest to monitor my slow, labored breaths.

The sentinel. She probably slept in my bed last night, so that she could hear any calls from the little boys' room. Or any calls from my hospital room. She'd been waiting for news since yesterday afternoon, when she brought the kids home from an outing at the park and found Reed's note on the kitchen counter: Kathy's water broke.

The telephone waited on the bedside table. Next to it rested the plastic calling card Mom bought for me when this all started. Over the past two weeks I'd clocked a dozen or more hours on that card, making the rounds, telling everyone the story: Preterm labor. Four centimeters. Hospital bed rest. Each time I delivered the news I was rewarded with a little gasp coming from the phone receiver, a little piece of my crisis absorbed by proxy. Call by call, I parceled out the shock and fear as if I were dealing a pack of cards. And nobody was more willing to take a loaded hand than my mother.

I dialed my house. Mom answered right away.

"You have a new grandson," I said.

"Oh, Kathy! Congratulations!" Her crisis voice. I'd heard it too many times—worry wound tight, like dental floss around a fingertip, so tight it squeaked with fake cheer. "How is he?"

"He's doing okay." Pause. "He's breathing a lot better than we expected him to."

"Oh, thank goodness. That's wonderful, sweetie!" I could

almost hear the whoosh of stress releasing from her neck and shoulders. "How big is he?"

"Four pounds, three ounces."

"Really? He gained a whole pound in the hospital? Oh, I'm so glad he's okay."

This would never work. I had to speak before her muscles unwound one more turn. I cleared my throat, dredging up words.

"Mom, he has Down syndrome."

Pause.

"He does?" The pitch of her voice fell an octave. Long seconds of silence, then she gave a resolute sigh. "Well, Kathy, he must have come to your family for a good reason."

I flinched. Like many other Mormons, Mom and I believed God chooses certain children to be born with disabilities, and sends those children to specific families. In other words, Thomas was handpicked to have Down syndrome, and I was handpicked to be his mother. This whole situation was supposedly a blessing. But to my shame, it didn't feel like one. And I couldn't bring myself to say so, not even to my mother.

I ended the conversation as quickly as I could, then rolled onto my side, wishing I could stay in bed forever. Mom, by contrast, would've hit the floor running if she were me. Nothing stopped that woman. Throughout her divorce from my father, her remarriage, and her struggle to blend two troubled families, she clung fiercely to hope, smiling when others would cry, or scream. Her emotional endurance seemed superhuman. This strength I loved, and hated—loved because it made me feel safe, hated because it made me feel lonely.

So lonely.

I picked up the phone again and called Kate, my touchstone since high school, and a trained therapist to boot. As soon as I heard her firm, warm voice I began to relax, as if she were sitting right next to me, holding my hand.

"Thomas has Down syndrome," I said.

"Oh, babe," she sighed. She began emotional triage, gathering all the pieces of the crisis as quickly as I could unpack them. Thomas's well-being was the chief concern—his health, even his survival. But there were many other players: my husband, my children. Myself. We, too, had urgent needs. Kate laid these pieces out, arranged them, studied them one by one.

"This is big," she said.

"Yes." I closed my eyes. Kate would take care of me.

Then, from somewhere in the background over Kate's shoulder, I heard a clatter and a happy shout—her children were awake. I opened my eyes, surprised by the obvious: Kate wasn't here. She was standing in her kitchen, two thousand miles away. Her children were probably climbing on the table, spilling the milk and Cheerios, taking advantage of their distracted mother. And soon, very soon, she would hang up the phone, mop up the milk, and get on with her life, which was not mine.

Kate promised to call later that evening. After we hung up, I felt so empty that I picked up the phone again and called another friend, my longtime confidante who was newly pregnant with her fifth child.

"The baby has Down syndrome," I said with a nervous laugh. The week before, she and I had been talking about the roll of the dice every couple makes at conception, and she mentioned a television news segment she'd just seen about children with Down syndrome. "You see things like that," she said, "and you think, 'Please, no.'"

Please, no. I pictured her standing with one hand on the phone and the other shielding her abdomen. I could hear her crying in sympathy, and likely in fear and gratitude as well—fear that the same thing might happen to her, gratitude that it probably wouldn't. I knew well that shameful relief which can come when tragedy strikes a friend, that sense of escape: Since it happened to her, it's less likely to happen to me.

It had happened to me. I had a son with Down syndrome;

she did not. Kate did not. My mother did not. And it wouldn't matter how many phone calls I made, how many times I told the tale. I was holding cards I couldn't give away.

AN HOUR LATER I stripped off my soiled gown and stepped gingerly into the shower stall. I turned the water on full blast, as hot as I could bear, and stood directly under the spray. The water around my feet ran rusty with washed-off blood.

Six times before I'd stood like this, ravaged and spent, letting the hot water run until it was gone, avoiding the moment when I'd have to step out of the shower and into a daunting new life. As much as I'd loved and wanted each of my newborns, the postpartum period was always hell. Raging hormones, bleeding nipples. Thick, black exhaustion. A certain despair that only comes when you feel dead, yet must keep others alive. With Sam, those weeks had included an extra layer of stress from the NICU stay, with its beeping monitors and needle-wielding nurses and thick, heavy air. All of this was waiting for me on the other side of the shower curtain—and it was only the beginning.

Ellen, my close friend from high school, has a brother with Down syndrome. He was little—two or three years old—when I first met him. His dirty blond hair was cut page-boy style; his thick glasses magnified his gray eyes, making him look constantly astonished. But he seemed foreign to me, distasteful, even less appealing than typical kids with their crusty noses and constant demands. Ellen loved to play with him. She even got scolded by her mother once for dressing him up in girl clothes and makeup, then posing him for photographs. I laughed when I saw the photos of David in drag, but I couldn't imagine loving such a brother. Not the way I loved my own brother, who was part of me, like a limb.

Could I love such a son?

I rubbed my arms and legs with a rough washcloth, determined to scrub away not only dirt and sweat and oil, but also doubt. Of course I could love Thomas. I already did. I loved him as I'd loved each of my new babies, with a primal strength full and fierce. My friends and family members couldn't share the burden of his disability, but they couldn't share this intense bond either. Not even my mother could.

Yet the bond wouldn't be enough, not for long. It was instinctual. Even animal. Thomas deserved human love, the delight and appreciation and tenderness one unique person feels for another. I'd never felt this for a person with Down syndrome or any other disability. I didn't know if I could.

Goosebumps rose on my arms—the hot water was gone. And my time to indulge in weakness was gone. I would make myself be whatever I had to be. A child waited in a plastic box down the hall, and six more were waiting at home, waiting for security to surround them like a warm mantle, soft yet strong. Waiting for their mother.

How the Prayers Ran Dry

EMILY SUMMERHAYS

FROM *Sunstone*

SOMETIMES I PRAY with my eyes wide open. And sometimes with one of those eyes on the television, just for good measure. Not because I'm particularly absorbed in that Downy commercial but because I don't want God to think he has my full attention. Childish, I know.

When I was a child, I prayed as a child, with my eyes screwed tightly shut, arms folded firmly against my body, speaking in slow, taut tones, as if I could command divine attention through a sheer critical mass of rigidity. I carefully balanced the ratio of blessings asked to blessings thanked for. I spoke of moisture instead of rain. I used all of my thee's and thou's correctly, and, approximating the sonorous tones of my elders, asked to be both nourished *and* strengthened.

At least, that's how I prayed in front of people. It was, of course, all just for show—something I'd picked up in church. Something to trot out at mealtimes and in Sunday School. Because that's what reverence looked like in sacrament meeting and sounded like in Primary, and I suppose I thought that's what reverence must feel like—at least, to other people. But to me, outside of church and in my own world, reverence was something completely different.

In those days, I was the embodiment of having a prayer in one's heart. Though loquacious on the surface, I was not much given to giving up my true thoughts. But the song of the righteous flowed freely through my limbs and through my mind and sometimes flew right out of my mouth when no one was around to hear it. I walked around in constant conversation with myself and with my Creator. We had long, rambling talks that had neither beginning nor end. Each new day took up where the previous had left off, often in the middle of the thought that had drifted away with me into sleep. In those days, reverence felt like whispering secrets to your sister in the dark. It felt like walking barefoot, hand in hand, over cool, shaded grass. In those days, reverence felt like friendship. And freedom. It felt like safety. And love. And not much at all like "reverence."

In those days, prayer was not an "ask and ye shall receive" sort of thing. It wasn't a method for getting what I needed, or even really for showing gratitude or respect. Not to me. Prayer, in those days, was simply a way of connecting. To what, I doubt I ever paused to articulate, any more than I ever really paused to articulate any of those heavenly exchanges—I only know that it worked. I felt connected, and the connection was comfortable, so easy. In those days, I could slip into slumber knowing I was loved and watched over, that I was important, and that everything would be all right in the end. I never asked for much, not in those days. Perhaps I did not ask then because I did not then need.

Until one day when I was about eight years old, playing on my first soccer team, and my jersey went missing just before gametime. Mom was jingling the car keys at me in frustration as I frantically searched my floor, my closet, my drawers, but came up empty. As I rifled through my belongings, I tossed a hasty, heartfelt prayer heavenward: *Heavenly Father, please please please help me find my jersey, Mom's gonna kill me.*

And then, my first Impression. Just like everyone talks about in testimony meeting. Against all logical inclination, I searched my pajama drawer (which, just like everyone talks about in testimony meeting, I had already thoroughly—or so I thought—searched). There, at the bottom, beneath a nightshirt I despised so much I never wore it, lay my jersey. And there, just like everyone talks about in testimony meeting, sprouted a little testimony.

From that time forward, I became obsessed with the doctrinal ins and outs of prayer. With a waxy, day-glo orange highlighter, I marked every scriptural passage I could find that referred to asking and receiving, knocking and being opened unto. I began to wonder what faith that moves mountains might feel like and if that faith dwelt inside me. But I also discovered that it was imperative not to "ask amiss," and I puzzled over what that might mean. In the years that followed the Day I Lost and Found My Jersey, I became a miniature expert on prayer and felt that I harbored some of the mysteries of God safely in my heart, along with that comfy old reverence and encapsulated by that easy, foundational friendship.

BUT AS CERTAINLY as my house was built upon the Rock, the rains did come down, and the floods did come up.

Mom had always been my hero, of course, in the way that all mothers are heroes to their children. She had golden hair and golden ideals and golden achievements. She ran marathons and kept a spotless house. She made family dinners and had a scientific career. She raised four children: honor students, all-state athletes, missionaries, "nice kids" (made even more amazing by the fact that I was in my early teens). She baked brownies. She saved lives. She made countless school projects out of salt-dough and Popsicle sticks. Everyone on our street envied her perfect flowerbeds. She had faith in herself and in hard work and Providence, and she was always there to lean on.

And then, she wasn't.

But it began slowly. At first, there was an occasional hitch in her step. Later, a frequent furrow in her brow. Soon, she was walking around with a hand jammed into her side, as though trying to hold the pain to one spot. My prayers began to grow worried.

As the disease worsened, my faith became more necessary and, therefore, more fervent. I was determined to ask in faith, nothing wavering, for the answers I needed. And what I needed was to know how to help her. I wasn't asking for big-time miracles. I wasn't expecting a healing. The bulk of my faith was fixed on the doctors. The ones who would fix her. There was no need to pull out the big guns. I sought instead to find ways to ease her pain. I gave her a journal to help her occupy her mind while she was physically incapacitated. She never wrote in it. To make sure she stayed out of the sun, I took over much of the gardening. But her love of mucking about in the dirt was so strong it made her foolish, and many were the days that I found her, near-fainted, in the yard, with muddy knees. Every night I prayed, with increasing urgency, as something inside me began to tremble.

I was about eighteen the night my mother and I went into the kitchen for a glass of milk. She collapsed in front of me—just went down on the linoleum, neither folding nor crumpling gracefully like they do in the movies. I don't remember hearing her hit the floor, just the sound of spilled milk dripping steadily from the countertop. I dropped to my knees and screamed for my father.

Later that night, I dropped to my knees again and screamed silently for my Father in Heaven. *That's it,* I explained to him. *This is all we can take. This is rock bottom. You have to help us, please. Please. I don't know what to do. Make her better. Make me better. Make* something *better.*

But it wasn't rock bottom—not by a long shot—it only got worse. My mother could hardly bear the weight of her own shrinking frame. Disease had left her body weak, her skin paper-thin and dark with bruising. The holes in her thoughts and sentences grew as the medication slowly leached her memory away. She could not stand at a counter long enough to cook. She could not sit long enough to go to the movies. She could not run, she could not work, she could not drive, and perhaps worst of all, she could not go out in the sun.

Every morning I left the house in fear, and every evening I returned directly to my mother's bedroom, just to make sure she was all right.

All was never right, but there were often golden moments. I spent hours on her bed, reading her my school papers, telling her about the things I did with my friends, making plans with her for the garden. Some days I would come home to find her in a nightgown the color of Crayola sunshine, dancing to *Bon Jovi*. Some days she'd ask me to take her out for a chocolate-chocolate donut. Those moments were precious gifts. But I wanted more than just a few minutes of happiness.

In classic type-A fashion, I determined that all of this was some sort of divine test and that I was failing it. I reevaluated the way I prayed and decided I must be doing something wrong. I revisited all those scriptures I'd discovered in my early fervor, and decided that I was somehow asking amiss. "Yea, I know that God will give liberally to him that asketh. Yea, my God will give me, if I ask not amiss" (2 Nephi 4:35). "Ye ask, and receive not, because ye ask amiss, that ye may consume it upon your lusts" (James 4:3).

I knew I wasn't asking to satisfy any lusts for personal gain. I didn't think I was asking anything for myself, really. So maybe it was my attitude. Something fundamentally wrong with my approach. Perhaps my hitherto informal prayer habits weren't, after all, what an omnipotent God wanted from me. So I resurrected rigid "reverence" and humble formality. I tried to pray as formulaically and worshipfully and as kneeling-by-the-bed-ly as possible, just like the pictures in the *Ensign*, as if those prayers could be somehow more potent. Any port in a storm.

To avoid being too much of a drain on the divine storehouse of blessings, I saved up my requests for the very most important things and never asked anything for myself. Not for help on my finals, not for comfort in other trials (and there were many other hardships, physical and financial, with which my family, like all others, had to contend). I directed all my faith toward this one problem, determined somehow to solve it. Nevertheless, my prayers fell crumpled into my lap, one by one, time after time. Each request returned to sender.

Having at length concluded that my faith *wasn't* apparently good enough to move mountains, I reasoned that it must be that I had (or maybe my mother had) something else to learn. I squared my shoulders. If life was to be a test, I was going to "pass." As the years went by, I offered up to the Lord all the things I had learned about life and love and family and faith and compassion and hope and dignity and sorrow and patience and suffering and on and on and on, as if at last, the "right" answer would click open the lock that had kept my mom in pain, and finally set my family free.

I was tired, spirit-sore, weary, and wary, and at the bottom of it all, I had a hard time believing in the weight of my prayers. Deep down, I thought the fault was mine. I felt like a pathetic annoyance, as though my heartfelt, faith-drenched pleas sounded like so many "are we there, yets?" to my Father in Heaven. I began to feel as if God's reception of my prayers must be something along the lines of, "What, *you* again? *This* again?"

Never one to want to put others out, I stopped asking.

For anything.

Who can sway the mind of God? Not me, apparently.

I had no real belief in the efforts of others, either. In fact, when others offered to pray for my mother, I would smile and nod and wish they'd just pick up the phone and call her instead. It would have taken about as much time, yet meant so much more to her. Especially since I had, by then, finished school and left home. Had, in fact, escaped, after a fashion, into the relative freedom of my own emerging life. Leaving her that much more lonely in her bed, in her garden, and in her pain. My escape was imperfect, however, burdened as I still was with daily reminders of my spiritual impotence and with an overwhelming sense of responsibility. It was *my* faith, after all, that had failed.

THE DAY THE PRAYERS finally ran dry was one that, ironically, had nothing much to do with my mother. I was twenty-five years old, staring into a computer screen, watching in real time as my baby brother's last hopes finally came crashing to earth. As I watched in queasy silence, I could almost hear milk dripping steadily onto the kitchen floor.

He and I had spent our earliest years at each other's throats, our teen years as bosom buddies, and all of those years, both good and bad, playing catch in the backyard. The rhythmic sound of a baseball slapping into leather very often took on an angry cast, but mostly it was like the ticking of some great cosmic clock, measuring out our growing strength and strengthening bond. At first, I barely put up with his ineptitude. He was too young, too little, and far too annoying. We usually did more fighting than throwing, more hitting than catching. But necessity bound us together, and eventually love for the game taught us love for each other. When the house became too silent, we'd grab our mitts and head outside. When Mom's struggle became oppressive, we'd find a ball and hit the grass. When we couldn't talk, we'd throw. We became each other's haven. The oasis in the desert. The calm in the eye of the storm.

It soon became apparent, not just to me but to everyone who saw him move, that my brother was a Natural. Chock-full of God-given talent. But riddled with physical limitations. When he had his first knee surgeries, at age thirteen, I brought him jelly beans and helped him oil his new glove. In later years, I stood in the place of my mother, who all too often couldn't stand: I drove him to physical therapy, picked him up from practice, and watched his orthopedic surgeon drain syringe after syringe full of bloody fluid from his legs. In spite of it all, though, joy radiated from him when he took the field. Troubles at home melted into the background when I watched him go up to bat, and seeing him run the bases was testimony enough of miracles.

In time, his life became like a story from the *Children's Friend.* He was scouted by the majors. He was offered big-time scholarships. He was flown around the country to investigate his prospects. And yet, he was humble. A gentle giant. No one was more kind, more generous. No one was more dedicated, more single in purpose. No one worked as hard or sacrificed so much. And then he sacrificed it all. He laid all that—his past and his future, the only thing he'd ever wanted or truly loved—on the altar of faith. He told them all, "No," and went on a mission.

Like Abraham, he was ultimately spared the usual outcome of that particular sacrifice. Stanford University held a place for him and welcomed him to the team, two years older, two years wearier, and two years out of shape. But he blew out his knee in the second week. More surgeries, more miseries; more prayers, more pain.

I could see it all unfolding. I fought fate on two fronts now.

When he made a miraculous recovery after an entire year of intensive physical therapy and was drafted by the Mariners, I began to think that, though God had closed the door on my mom, perhaps he'd opened up wide the windows of heaven to pour out my brother's blessings. It would almost have been worth it.

But again, he sacrificed. He did the sensible thing, turned down the major leagues, and finished his degree. He was stronger than he'd been in years, faster and surer on his legs, hitting harder and striding longer. The majors would come around again next year.

Except—they didn't.

All that God-given talent.

Well. They say the Lord giveth, and the Lord taketh away.

Draft day came and went, the wonders of modern technology

allowing me to watch from 3,000 miles away as his dreams—and mine, and my mother's—finally hit the floor. The career-ending back injury was still some months away, but that day had truly been the end. In more ways than one.

That day, I dared to pray for him. All that day. I threw the last drops of my faith down, like a gauntlet, before my God, and relived in that one afternoon a microcosm of the previous ten years, moving from tentative to urgent to despairing to, ultimately, broken.

That day, I withdrew my broken heart and instead gave God a not-very-contrite finger.

But even that, I think now, was a kind of prayer.

For months, sick to my stomach on anger and hurt, I told myself I didn't believe. I walked around with my emotional fists balled up, holding my spirit in tight. For months, I ignored God, knowing all the while that one cannot "ignore" something, some-*one*, whom one doesn't believe exists. I ignored that, too. Childish, I know.

When I was a child, I'd prayed as a child, in innocence, in earnestness, in thoughts, letters, songs, wishes, and yes, even curses. I'd understood as a child, and thought as a child, but now I am a woman grown, and it is time to put away childish things.

A FEW MONTHS AGO, a friend told me she had been praying for me. As has become my habit, I smiled and nodded and had no idea what to say. "Thank you" seemed inadequate even while protestations that I didn't really believe in prayer bubbled up under the gratitude.

I knew why she'd been praying. I've been sick.

As with my mother, it had begun slowly, with unexplainable aches and pains. I walked a bit too slowly, too stiffly, too carefully. The smudges under my eyes grew more pronounced. My doctors told me what they told my mother all those years ago, and whenever I think of her now, I can see the spectre of my possible future. I think of spilt milk and muddy knees. I think of nightgowns in the afternoon and pills, morning, noon, and night. I think of my brother and me slipping out the back door to try to play like normal kids. I think of our trying to escape the dual prisons of our silent house and our mother's frail body. But there's no escaping it now. For any of us.

I knew why my friend had been praying: because she loved me and because she was scared. In its purest form, prayer is simply an act of love; the first and last bastion of the impotent, the worried, the scared. And while I couldn't quite share it, I also couldn't deride her faith. I couldn't even shrug it off with the usual vacant smile and distracted nod. Instead, I loved her right back. In that moment, as she gazed at me with unfeigned compassion in her eyes and declared her faith with a complete lack of self-consciousness, I saw myself as I once had been—as I'm not sure I can ever be again—and those spiritual fists I'd clenched up so very tightly began to ease. The anger and hurt and fear began to drain away, replaced by the faintest glow of gratitude, and from the ruins of my childhood prayers, something new began to emerge: not quite faith, but a tiny hope; not quite a prayer, but the barest wish for one.

Over subsequent months, that first wish grew and multiplied. My husband had a crucial presentation to make. A ward member got a frightening diagnosis. A neighbor family struggled financially. Through it all, I wished that I could pray. A friend watched her father slowly die. Another lost a brother to an accident. Still another endured a dangerous pregnancy. I wished with all my heart that I could give them the words, *I'll pray for you.* I wished to the point of tears that I could do it, but I couldn't, quite. Not then. Not yet. I just ... couldn't.

But still, that wish was there. Someday I might again be able to pray for something that really matters; but for now, I practice over pancakes and lasagna. Mealtimes and sacrament meeting, Sunday School and bedtime.

Sometimes, now, I pray—with my eyes wide open. And sometimes, yes, one of those eyes is trained on the television. I guess you could say that I'm spiritually skittish. But sometimes, now, out of the corner of my eye, I can almost see myself clearly again. I can almost see that girl who talks to God, liberally, and upbraideth not.

We Who Owe Everything to a Name

LYNDA MACKEY WILSON

FROM *BYU Studies*

WHEN I WAS TEN YEARS OLD, my mother told me that my father was not really my father. My "real father" was a man named Aladdin, a foreign student at UC Berkeley where mom had been a student. When his father found out that he had gotten an American girl pregnant he whisked Aladdin back home.

I found this interesting. I tucked it into a mental drawer labeled "intriguing data" and went out to play. It did explain some things. Like why I was olive-skinned with jet-brown eyes and dark hair when my little sister was blond and blue-eyed. But it was not in the drawer labeled "disturbing facts." All the unpleasant things about growing up in my family were related to my mother.

Finding out that I had a father somewhere in the Middle East had a kind of exotic appeal when I thought about it—which was rare. You see, I already had a father. His name was John Joseph Mackey. He was a retired Catholic from Boston, the son of Irish immigrants, and he was the most real thing in my life. Not for a second did I ever think, 'Oh no, that means that Daddy is not really my father.'

He was my Father. He was my rock. He taught me. He spent time with me. He told me jokes. He took me for rides on his big BMW motorcycle. On Saturday mornings, we went out for pancakes. He complimented me. He protected me. He smiled at me. He told me that I was smarter than he was and that I could do anything I wanted to. I didn't think anybody could be smarter than my father, but I knew it meant he believed in me. All the mental health I gratefully draw on in my adult years comes from the security of knowing that my father really loved me.

It took me years to realize what an amazing thing he had done.

During the time my mother and father were dating at Berkeley, my dad took off for a two-month course at UCLA. He didn't tell her he was leaving or that he was coming back. She wasn't an important part of his life then. But he was everything in her thumping heart. Devastated, she drowned her sorrows in the elixir of Physical Attraction. Aladdin asked her out. I don't know how many times they dated, but one day my father called and said "I'm back." No big deal.

Except that she was pregnant. She told Jack she was pregnant with his child. He did the honorable thing and offered to marry her. They tied the knot during a break between classes. She told me later of the last time she ever prayed. "Please Lord, let this be Jack's baby."

She knew in the delivery room. I was a little Arab from the start. Dark hair, nearly black eyes and olive skin. But she admitted nothing. Trust being crucial in marriage, this made for a bad beginning. Dad wasn't stupid and later, when my little sister was born, the comments by Dad's friends started: "Milkman stop by when you were away?" My sister and I did not look like sisters. Sometime during my childhood my mother blurted out in the middle of a blowup, "OK. She's not your kid. Does that make you happy!"

I didn't know any of it. I only knew two basic things about growing up in my family. My father loved me. And my mother didn't. In the work I've done since to sort through it all and forgive as Christ requires, I think of her, pregnant and seventeen, scared to death. It was all so doomed.

She was not abusive in the way that lands kids in the ER. She ignored me. She didn't like to look at me. I was her sin walking around on knock-kneed legs. Aladdin must have been knock-kneed like me, because no one else had them.

"Mom, will you show me how to work the sewing machine?"

"Can't. I'm busy."

"Mom. Can you help me make brownies?"

"Don't have time."

Most of the time, being ignored is not life-threatening. Just enraging. There was lots of anger at my mother. Diary pages of "I hate my mother!" in neat rows.

There was just one fact that didn't fit with the otherwise bad soap opera script. My father didn't care that I wasn't carrying his genes. He had decided to be my father. I see now that he adopted me—a de facto adoption. He made me his from the beginning. He never took out his anger at my mother's betrayal of him on me. Because I was his daughter.

Like a duckling imprinting on Momma duck, I imprinted on my father. I absorbed his likes and dislikes, his taste in music, his politics, his love of reading and education, and even his bent for writing. To me, he seemed to know everything worth knowing. So all my little neurons did their darndest to line up and fire just like his: I got good grades, wrote a lot, read everything from the cereal box in the morning to the under-the-cover-with-the-flashlight library book at night. He was a Democrat and voted for Adlai Stevenson. I proudly wore my Vote for Adlai button to school in Shreveport, Louisiana. I tried to *be* him.

I was bathing seven times in the river of my father's mind—all except for one last dip. Some guardian angel held me by the heel, and I did not get immersed in my father's religion. That religion was the one he learned at Berkeley and taught at most other universities in the 40's after the war—Darwin, Freud, Marx, Joyce, Kinsey. It was modern and therefore sophisticated, and it scoffed—politely in those days—at anything that made religion real and concrete, whether that was the Virgin Mary appearing at Lourdes or the Angel Moroni handing a boy golden plates to translate.

When I was eleven, we moved near my maternal grandparents, who loved me too. They were active in the LDS church. I took the streetcar to their house. I had lots of questions about life, death, and God. I think I was born a theologian.

That was the year my parents gave my sister and me a Time-Life book for Christmas called *The Origins of Life*. There were dramatic pictures of lightning flashing over moody ammonia seas, doing the Darwinian equivalent of thundering, "Let there be life!" The book was filled with dinosaurs and proto-humans. It was my parents' attempt to proselyte for their agnosticism. If they worried about their oldest daughter's odd propensity to think about God, I'm sure they thought that time and a college education would cure the malady.

I loved my dad with all my heart, but it was not my fate to absorb modern agnosticism from two parents who had rejected the religions of their youth. I had a not-to-be-denied hunger to know if there was a God and, if there was, what he was like.

From my grandparents, I heard the Plan of Salvation for the first time. Actually, my grandmother drew it for me on the blackboard in her kitchen: a circle for pre-mortality, a wavy line for the veil of forgetfulness, another circle for earth, and so on. I also checked out a series of books from the library called "*Why I Am A _____*" (*Methodist, Lutheran,* and so forth). You see, one of my father's predominant traits was intellectual honesty. I was not about to believe what my grandparents believed just because it sounded so right and I hoped it were true. My father's daughter felt an obligation to gather data and to be careful.

Perhaps the most important thing my grandparents taught me

was that if you asked God a question, he could and would answer you. That seemed like a reasonable thing, a good test. I began to pray. I would sit in my backyard and talk to God, if there was a God, and ask him, if he could hear me, to answer me, if he would, by letting me know he was there, if he wanted to. Finally I stopped equivocating and proposed a bold plan that he could show me he existed by letting the giant concrete cross on Mt. Davidson appear through the fog the next morning. I ended up asking for this sign more than once because one clear day could be just a coincidence.

Some days were foggy, and some days weren't. I kept praying and began to be less dogmatic. "Please just let me know if you're there!"

One day, while I was riding the streetcar in San Francisco, God talked back. I simply had a download of the spirit into my eleven-year-old heart that was undeniable. Like the moment when the Blue Fairy touched a wooden puppet and Pinocchio turned into a real boy, nothing after that was ever the same. I looked up startled and had to resist a momentary urge to run down the streetcar aisle yelling, "God answered me! He's real!"

I think I was prepared to accept the gospel precisely because of my relationship with my father. Fathers were wonderful things. A Heavenly Father was more of the same on a grander scale, with infinitely greater power to provide, protect, and defend. At eleven, I asked to be baptized. My parents humored me and said OK, assuming I would grow out of this religious phase.

As a teenager, it was obvious that my Mormonism wasn't wearing off. My mother railed against her parents for brainwashing me, and my father just seemed confused. "How can a bright girl like you believe in angels and golden plates?" My mother told me she would help pay for college as long as I didn't go to BYU. So, of course, I went to BYU.

I went there in the early 70's. I graduated, married, and raised four children in the Church. I now have the pleasure of watching them raise their own children in the faith. Once I had a blessing from my grandfather in which he pronounced I would "do a work for [my] real father's people." The phrase "real father" made not the slightest dent in the relationship that had been my anchor. I already had a real father, and like the Velveteen Rabbit, it was love that made him real.

Yes, I have somewhere a biological father who passed on his physical DNA—the knock knees, large dark eyes, my height (I'm taller than my father). Then I have the father who loved and nurtured me. He is ninety years old now, his Irish wit still charming. I have proudly carried his name through my life.

But I bear more than his name. In many significant ways, I have become like him. I have taken into myself his ideas, his character, and his thought patterns. My children asked for stuff, and I lectured them: "A man is rich to the degree that he can walk through the market place of life and say, 'I don't need that. I don't need that.'" But really it was Dad's philosophizing. A guest in my home breaks a dish, and I say, "People are more important than things." But it is really my father talking to them. I am "the word" of my father. I reflect him outwardly to my children and in every association I ever have in this life. I owe everything to his name.

One day at my health club, I heard a stunning echo of this thought. I was listening to an audio course on the history of ancient Rome to numb the boredom of the treadmill. Suddenly I heard something that galvanized me. I never took Roman history in school. What I knew was mostly from Toga movies. I didn't know that when Mark Anthony read Caesar's will to the people of Rome, they learned he named a grandnephew, Gaius Octavius, as his adopted son. It was news to the boy as well as the public. He was 18 years old, practically a baby by Roman standards.

Here is what the professor said about Octavius: "He wasn't of particularly august origins. His natural father was a local from a town north of Rome, so he really didn't have any great connections. He had met Caesar once. Caesar had obviously been impressed about some qualities that he saw in the young man for he adopted him as his son in the will and made him his chief heir.

Now I should point out, that in Roman eyes, the legal adoption of a person gave that person every claim, not just to the property and patrimony of the adopting party but also to the heritage, the political connections, the name, the *dignitas*, everything else that came with the adoption. The Romans really made no serious distinction between a natural and an adopted son. It wasn't considered like the adopted son was an imposter or some kind of a late claimant. He was simply considered as if he had been born of the adopting party. And so Gaius Octavius, at that time when he became adopted, took the name Gaius Julius Caesar Octavianus."

Historians refer to him as Octavian, but he called himself Caesar, son of Caesar, and that name made all the difference. The men who had been loyal to Caesar flocked to him. Slowly his power grew. Inevitably Mark Anthony and Octavian clashed, fought and Anthony was beaten. Octavian became Augustus Caesar, the first emperor of Rome, the man who ordered the census that took Joseph and Mary to Bethlehem. Fascinating!

It was Cicero who recorded Mark Anthony's comment on their fates. Octavian was "that boy, who owes everything to a name!" The phrase reverberated in my mind and heart. Didn't I owe everything to a name? Hadn't my father given me the good life I had by making me his, by adopting me?

It was later that I discovered the Apostle Paul's use of the term adoption in reference to our relationship with Christ. The word adopt or adoption does not appear in the Old Testament, with its kinship obligations to orphans, nor is it found in the book of Mormon, whose laws and social customs were derivative of Mosaic Law. But Paul understood the implications of being an heir by adoption. He, though a Jew, was a Roman citizen in a Roman world. And he used the implications of Roman law to explain to the gentiles the inheritance they might receive through the gospel's new covenant in Christ's blood. "For ye have not received the spirit of bondage again to fear; but ye have received the Spirit of adoption, whereby we cry, Abba, Father" (Rom. 8:15).

Until I listened to that tape on Caesar's adoption of Octavian as his heir, this scripture puzzled me. Adopted by God? Weren't we, after all, his natural children. He was the real, "biological" if you will, father of our spirit bodies. We didn't need any adoption process to become God's children. I found Ephesians 1:5 later. "Having predestinated us unto the adoption of children by Jesus Christ to himself." Ah. It all began to make sense, especially to me, that child who was brought in out of the cold by a father who made me his.

It is Christ who makes us his heirs. He becomes our father, as King Benjamin explains: "Because of the covenant which ye have made ye shall be called the children of Christ. His sons, and his daughters; for behold, this day he hath spiritually begotten you… ye are born of him and have become his sons and his daughters" (Mosiah 5:7). That is why, contrary to the persistent but false doctrine we find popping up like a whack-a-mole in gospel doctrine classes, we do not "earn" exaltation. The word earn is never used in scripture to refer to the process by which men and women become exalted. To quote exactly from the LDS.org scripture search engine, "There were no occurrences of the word EARN found in the Text of the Scriptures." The word is "inherit." Stick the word "inherit" in the search box, and you get 251 hits.

Once I saw it, I saw it everywhere. Earning implies a *quid pro quo*, Latin for "something for something," and "indicates a more-or-less equal exchange of goods or services." An employee "earns" his wages because his work is worth twenty dollars an hour to his employer. But I did not earn my father's love. And Octavian did not earn the title of Caesar. Those who give the inheritance set the terms.

In our poor fallen humanness, what can we do which "earns" us the magnificent gift of Eternal Life? To earn something puts someone in our debt. But as King Benjamin made clear, God is never in our debt (Mosiah 2:21–22).

The inheritance is Christ's to give. He alone truly did earn it. His perfect life, without spot or blemish, with its complete submission to the will of his Father, earned "a fullness of the glory of the Father; and he received all power, both in heaven and on earth" (D&C 93:16-17). In all ways, he earned his exalted state. The miracle is that he is willing to make us his children, heirs of all he has.

To qualify, we covenant to obey him, take his name and always remember him. He said, "I am Alpha and Omega, the beginning and the end. I will give unto him that is athirst of the fountain of the water of life freely. He that overcometh shall inherit all things; and I will be his God, and he shall be my son" (Rev. 21:6).

I cling to these promises that make sense to me through the lens of my own life. My own father's love was a redeeming force for good in my life. That love makes it easy to believe in the redeeming love of our Savior, to whose name we owe everything.

Patriarchal Blessing

DARLENE YOUNG

FROM *Dialogue*

The boy, sixteen, is taller than his mother, taller than
the creaky man with shining eyes and trembling hands.

Mother comes fasting, something she's good at,
years of honing her physical yearnings
into empty bowls to catch spiritual manna.
And now she is empty of all but her hope
of hearing the voice of God through this old man.
Her son, the first-fruit of her labors,
a rough-cut stone but the best she could do—
and would God touch this stone with his finger?

Her son folds into the chair with a quick glance
at her, an echo of the glance he gave her long ago
the day he stood to join his father in the font.

And maybe now the father will join them
in spirit? She, longing, glances to the corners of the room.
The trembling hands are stilled on the boy's head,
as if the words of power give them weight—

the words that dart like lightning in the air
and dance upon her eyelids. She opens them
to watch the old man, ageless, shine like sun,
his voice a whisper still but piercing bright.

The mother sits and holds the hand of God—
for once she feels she's truly not alone
in her sweet knowledge of her son's good heart.
She weeps to hear God tell her of the man
he will become, this boy she's nursed with blood
and milk, and tears,
this boy, a shining sword, a man of God.

And in the silence when the blessing's done
the son stands up and shyly takes her hand.
The old man, feeble now, stands at the door,
winking in the glitter of the stars.
For days those flashing words will dance like sparks
around her ears, behind her eyes and in the air—
as if she walked with diamonds in her hair.

CONTRIBUTORS' NOTES

NEIL AITKEN was born in Vancouver, BC and has lived in Saudi Arabia, Taiwan, and various parts of western Canada and the United States. He is the author of *The Lost Country of Sight*, the winner of the 2007 Philip Levine Prize for Poetry, and has been published in *Crab Orchard Review*, *The Drunken Boat*, *Ninth Letter*, *Sou'wester*, and many other literary journals. With a computer science and mathematics degree from BYU–Provo, he worked for a number of years as a computer games programmer before pursuing graduate work in creative writing and English literature.

PHYLLIS BARBER received a Master of Fine Arts in creative writing from Vermont College and has taught in its writing program. Her autobiography, *How I Got Cultured*, won the 1991 Association of Writers and Writing Programs Prize for Creative Nonfiction and the 1993 Award for Best Autobiography from the Association for Mormon Letters

BRITTNEY CARMAN holds an MFA in creative nonfiction from the University of Idaho. Her work has appeared in *Borrowed Earth*, *Segullah*, and the *Black Warrior Review*. "Believing Owl, Saying Owl" was nominated for a Pushcart Prize.

JOHNNA BENSON CORNETT started writing poetry hoping it would lead to writing fiction. A fifth-generation Californian, she lives in Palo Alto with her husband and four children. She's a proud alumnus of UCLA, where she graduated Phi Beta Kappa with a linguistics degree. Johnna designed and manages the Segullah website, and considers any day she rides her bike a good day.

DARIN COZZENS grew up in Powell, Wyoming. He has been a finalist for both the Iowa Short Fiction Awards and Sarabande's Mary McCarthy Prize in Short Fiction. He teaches at Surry Community College in Dobson, North Carolina.

LISA TORCASSO DOWNING resides in Texas, where she is an assistant professor of English for Collin College. Her short fiction has appeared in *Sunstone*, *Dialogue*, and *Irreantum* and is featured in the anthology, *Millennium: Latter-day Fiction*. "Clothing Esther" was awarded the Association for Mormon Letters 2007 Award for short fiction.

JOSHUA FOSTER continues to live and work on his family's potato and grain farm in southeastern Idaho. He studied English and Spanish literature at BYU–Idaho and recently earned an MFA in fiction and nonfiction writing from the University of Arizona.

JAMES GOLDBERG, one of the nation's most promising young Caucajewmexdian authors, writes three blogs: one dealing with scripture (*mormonmidrashim.blogspot.com*), one dealing with ethnicity (*caucajewmexdian.blogspot.com*), and one dealing in surreality (*goldbergish.blogspot.com*). He is married to Nicole Wilkes and has one daughter.

ANGELA HALLSTROM received her MFA in fiction from Hamline University and teaches creative writing for Brigham Young University. She is the author of the novel *Bound on Earth* and serves as the co-editor of *Irreantum* magazine and on the editorial board of *Segullah*. She lives in South Jordan, Utah, with her husband and four children

LANCE LARSEN, Lance Larsen recently published his third poetry collection, *Backyard Alchemy* (University of Tampa, 2009). He has received a Pushcart Prize and a fellowship from the National Endowment for the Arts. One of his poems was included in *Best*

American Poetry 2009, and his prose has twice made the notable essays list in *Best American Essays 2005* and *2009*.

PATRICK MADDEN teaches creative nonfiction at Brigham Young University. *Quotidiana*, his book of personal essays, including "A Sudden Pull behind the Heart," will be published in early 2010 by the University of Nebraska Press. Visit *www.quotidiana.org* for his anthology of classical essays and other resources.

SCOTT RUSSELL MORRIS is a native of San Diego, California. He has a degree in recreation management and youth leadership from Brigham Young University. He is enthusiastic about essays, photography, food, and squirrels.

KATHRYN LYNARD SOPER is the author of *The Year My Son and I Were Born: A Story of Down Syndrome, Motherhood, and Self-Discovery*. She has edited four anthologies and serves as editor-in-chief of *Segullah: Writings by Latter-day Saint Women*. Kathryn lives with her husband, Reed, and their seven children in the mountain west; her website is *kathryn-lynardsoper.com*.

A native of the Salt Lake City area, EMILY SUMMERHAYS now lives in Manhattan, where she writes grants (among many other things) for the American Museum of Natural History. She holds an MA in English Literature and has worked as adjunct faculty in the English Department at the University of Utah. In her spare time, Emily contributes to the Feminist Mormon Housewives blog, sings for a pick-up band, and unabashedly reads trashy romance novels.

LYNDA WILSON lives in Northern California. She published her first book, *The Innkeeper's Wife* (Shadow Mountain) in 2006. She and husband, Larry, are the parents of four children.

She publishes a website, *www.sistersatthewell.org*, which provides group scripture study materials for LDS women.

DARLENE YOUNG serves as secretary for the Association for Mormon Letters and on the editorial board of *Segullah*. She lives in South Jordan with her husband and four sons. She is a recipient of a Utah Arts Council award. Now that the baby is in school, she hopes to enter an MFA program.